D1174238

The Winter Repertory
Michael Feingold / General Editor

the winter repertory

1

Kenneth Bernard

night club & other plays

INTRODUCTION: MICHAEL FEINGOLD

WINTER HOUSE LTD

NEW YORK

The author wishes to thank the following people and organizations for their help at one stage or another of these plays: Douglas Taylor, The Actors Studio, Steve Aaron and the New Theatre Workshop, Long Island University, Ellen Stewart and La MaMa E.T.C., The Wherehouse-La MaMa London Players, Beverly Grant, and especially John Vaccaro and the Play-House of the Ridiculous.

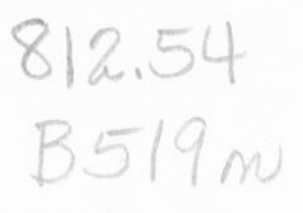

For Lucas, Judd,

and Kate

INTRODUCTION

"Destroy it?" Abbie Hoffman once wrote, querulously, about the giant plastic Toyland that is American culture. "Destroy it? Hell, we want to fuck in it!" Abbie's words might have come straight out of Kenneth Bernard's *Night Club,* so good is Mr. Bernard at capturing current American moods. The anarchic homiletics of America's favorite Yippie, and those of his many competitors for media attention, have certainly found their way into *Night Club,* into the shouts of the lewd-minded "audience" that provides the play with both actors and chorus, into the postures that audience goes through when it gets up onstage, and, most disturbingly, into the personality of that indefatigable phenomenon the audience addresses as Bubi.

In Bubi, Kenneth Bernard has created an Everything, a microcosmos within an all-inclusive metaphor. He (she? it?) speaks for the mob and to them, lectures, pleads with, punishes, submits to, intercedes for, controls, watches, celebrates, attacks, hates and loves them. All things to all men and women, Bubi changes roles with dazzling ease, a master traveler on that journey from mask to mask which is the true odyssey of "protean" twentieth-century man—a creature who may, or may not, hide some personal reality under the array of masks he parades before his equally identity-less fellow creatures.

They scream from the back of the house, "Strip, Bubi, Strip!" But is there anything underneath the thousand varieties of Bubi's behavior? You can't be sure. Didn't Peer Gynt think he saw the center of the onion for a second? Even Bubi isn't sure what he (misleading pronoun) is. Hence his tragedy. Nor would he tell us if he were sure, and lose his power over the Pavlovian crowd, desperate to know themselves through him. Hence his comedy. The terror of Oedipus and the gleeful triumph of Tartuffe: nowadays we like our genres mashed together.

I've started to write about *Night Club* in this hyperbolic vein because it's a work that can't be approached from the outside, as most plays can. It doesn't seem to have immediate predecessors in the dramatic tradition, as Kenneth Bernard's other plays, for all their demonic, violent individuality, nonetheless do. *The Moke-Eater,* with its violence suppressed and its language Englished up, might have been a Pinter play with a delicate no-exit ending. *The Giants in the Earth* has some sympathetic ancestors among army-base plays, and in the ghost stories of Algernon Blackwood. It isn't wholly accurate to call *The Monkeys of the Organ Grinder* naturalistic, but a naturalist-expressionist like Wedekind might have relished the grotesquerie of its lowlife characters and the wonderful, eccentric rhythms of their dialogue.

In each of these plays, there's the skeleton of a prior experience to cling to, should you feel you're losing your way, but *Night Club* is of itself, *sui generis,* unexpected. Its ostensible form is the homey, predictably-unpredictable one of the floor show, the cabaret revue, the Ed Sullivan Hour. But who could predict a floor show that included all of civilization in its devastating procession of acts, starting with the ventriloquial vagaries of the man-woman relationship and ending with a sudden-flash vision of tyranny and political execution? And even assuming that one could accept this charade by itself as a satiric picture of our world (which takes a pretty strong stomach), how is one to tolerate the other audience, that writhing mob in between the real spectators and the show—that mob from which the show emerges, first act by act and then *en bloc,* mass man apotheosized, humping away to the "William Tell" Overture?

I don't mean anything so simple as planting actors in the audience. We're on to that trick—we've seen the actors become the "audience" often enough. But seeing the audience become the actors is quite a different trip. We're seeing ourselves, in what must be the last outpost of the naturalist tradition in drama, seeing a thoroughly contemptuous picture of ourselves watching a show—and seeing it as part of a show that we're watching, meantime being assaulted by a flood of sensory experiences all around us: watching the show, watching the audience watch the show, listening to the deafening and virtually continuous rock music that fills the theater, shaken constantly by the mysterious noises—of construction, or is it destruction, or mobilization?—that attack from outside.

This performance is plainly meant to threaten our whole idea of ourselves, to dislocate our expectations with its endless, shifting textures of light and sound. Worst of all, our motives in going to the theater are so brought into question by the existence of that hideous other audience that, if we stay, we almost have to accept that floor-show view of our lives as the truth. And at this point in history, few can walk out on such wicked fascination. We live, as Americans, in a plastic metaphor for reality anyway; at *Night Club* we are trapped in a smaller, tighter-meshed version of that metaphor. And even when we finally escape, we meet ourselves coming back from Bubi's Hide-Away into the larger world theater, and wonder when we'll be asked to pay our cover charge.

Thus Kenneth Bernard's distinction as a playwright: He may ask the traditional questions of Western drama, about the nature of civilization and the purpose of man, but he poses them in the form of metaphors immediately accessible to us. Seeing his plays, one sees, not an example of something, or a dialectic to follow, or an action which one is obliged to distance oneself from and interpret, but the thing itself, the higher image, that speaks to us directly. In the case of *Night Club,* the image is simply carried a bit further—instead of seeing it happen, one is obliged to live in it or leave.

It makes sense that two of Mr. Bernard's major plays have been presented by the Play-House of the Ridiculous. The work of this group, and of its director John Vaccaro, is not easily described, or even easy to respond to in performance, full of flash and extravagance though it may be. The company is a set not of actors but of artificially heightened personalities, living out their chosen self-dramatizations through the convenience of someone else's play. Thus, instead of the two traditional elements of theater called "actor" and "character," the audience is confronted with "personality" (the performer's creation), and with "act" (the playwright's invention)—materials that would seem more appropriate to vaudeville or variety entertainment than to drama. They are, of course, the very stuff of the night club floor show.

And Vaccaro, as director, is as much the organizer and ringmaster of the whole show as he is instructor, interpreter, and so forth. At times—you can see it in his rehearsal behavior—he reminds one more of the harassed theater manager in a movie about backstage life than of any director as we usually understand the term. His mission is to keep everything going—the script, the performance of each act on the bill, the atmosphere of the theater—so as to guarantee the audience three full rings of entertainment at every moment. Rather than directing your response toward one goal and one fulfillment, he uses the materials at his disposal to keep you spinning. This is the Ridiculous: Goals are nonsense and fulfillment is a dirty joke. Hence the imperturbably mad lighting plot for *Night Club,* with its huge colored spotlights perpetually wandering over audience and stage, never resting except to make an incidental point called for in the script, appearing and disappearing till no one could know where to look next. That disorientation is the quintessence of Ridiculous achievement.

But there is no point to being John Vaccaro and inviting audiences to experience the Ridiculous if you have no genuinely Ridiculous experience to offer them, and for that a text, a shape for the show, material for the acts, is required. Some theater creators (Grotowski, for one) devise their own, but this causes a certain imbalance, unless the creator is equally gifted at writing words and at setting them in motion; he rarely is. John Vaccaro, more honest in this line than some of his colleagues, has never tried to put his own words on the stage. He once nearly gave up directing altogether—but then Fate, Ridiculous as ever, sent Kenneth Bernard his way.

The Moke-Eater, with which that collaboration began, is a deceptive play, just suited to what the Ridiculous was searching for at the time, a booby-trapped song of innocence to match the seemingly complex (but in truth terrifyingly simple) song of experience that is *Night Club.* In *The Moke-Eater,* according to one Ridiculous press release, Kenneth Bernard and the company "preside over the death of America." There is, of course, no actual death in the play. The victim, Jack, leaves the small town, shaken but alive, drives off, and reaches the next town only to discover that he is in the same place: Death-in-life.

The "death" that he observes, the sacrifice of the Old Man to "the Moke-Eater," is likewise of an indeterminate kind: The Old Man may remain alive after his agony; the whole thing is just a show, put on for visitors, infinitely repeatable at any hour of the day or night; day and night themselves are merely constructs of the townspeople's consciousness. The end is the beginning, and the Old Man will be there to hobble down the street and get beaten up by the mob as before: Death-in-life.

Night Club being a conspectus of civilization in general, *The*

Moke-Eater may be taken as dealing with that part of civilization which survives on innocence: America, where, as we know from the behavior of our present government, violent acts are detached from their traditional moral consequences by a false image of serenity. The town of Monte Waite is Mr. Bernard's corrective to that traditional image of the small town found in Thornton Wilder and other of our image-makers (*Cf.* the films of Frank Capra): the haven of democracy, honesty, love, beauty, and truth; the star of Norman Rockwell's *Saturday Evening Post* covers.

It should be emphasized that Mr. Bernard does not expose the American small town purely for the sake of exposing. That kind of criticism, too, is a part of our consciousness. Wilder's plays are defended as having a fundamentally pessimistic spirit; against the films of the 30s one could hold up Lewis' *Main Street* and a dozen other novels of village unhappiness; for every cheery Norman Rockwell, the public is offered a grim-faced Andrew Wyeth. The objection to that sort of negativism is precisely the one a Congressman from Nebraska (or Vermont) might raise: It's simple negativism. Elitist, city-versus-country stuff. But the author of *The Moke-Eater* has neatly made his urbanized hero the other side of the small-town coin: the ambitious, condescending city slicker, the proverbial traveling salesman, the get-up-and-go fellow with the take-the-money-and-run technique. Only he finds that the town cannot be sold so easily as he thinks, that it has a claim on him as well, and deeper than he cares to admit. He may think himself Jack, but after they have insisted on his being Fred for a certain length of time, he has to concede that in some way he is indeed their "Fwed," one of them come home after a successful foray in the big time.

Jack-Fred's dilemma is simple: when he stays there, he suffers, as Americans suffer at home. And the one time he escapes—to go to the bathroom, of course—he finds himself lost in a different world, among those exemplars of aristocratic barbarity (seen wonderfully as through American peasant eyes), the Harringtons, father and daughter, rulers of polite society—and eaters of human flesh. No chance of escape there.

The old civilization is class war, aristocratic barbarism; the new civilization, America, is repression and political violence by day, unexampled grotesquery and horror by night, when those of us who think we can avoid participation are forced to wait (the name of the town again: Monte Waite) and watch. Jack, the man of our time, the audience's link to the action, is compact of paradoxes. The city slicker as nebbish or gull (a Buster Keatonish archetype), he is also the spectator as victim, condemned to hear of and see the horrors that have created him and brought him where he is. *Our Town* has been rewritten, as it were, by Artaud.

Mentioning Artaud is to the point, though I don't mean to suggest that Kenneth Bernard's plays derive from a conscious desire to imitate Artaud's theatrical projects. The great visionary of modern French theater did attempt, as Bernard also does, to devise metaphors that surround an audience and communicate to it viscerally rather than intellectually. But Artaud's visions—*The Conquest of Mexico* and the like—may fail to affect us due to their self-conscious exoticism; they have an anthropological taint, and lack an emotional connection, for his readers. What's Mexico to a Chicagoan?

It's Kenneth Bernard's gift, on the other hand, to have discovered his images within us. He speaks, as Artaud does, of the falsity of civilization, the instability and hollowness of personality, the return of the savage gods of instinct. But the civilization he describes belongs to our own myths: The Myth of Technological Progress, The Myth of the Small Town as Paradise, The Myth of the Pleasures of Culture and Sophistication. And the gods he summons return not from outside, not from Mexico or Bali, but from our own evil dreams. We had better learn to deal with them. Through his plays, we have a rare opportunity to try.

Michael Feingold

Above: Kenneth Bernard (right)
and director John Vaccaro confer at
a rehearsal of *Night Club*
Over: Vaccaro demonstrates
for the cast

Night Club
in rehearsal
Above left: Audience
Above right: Timmy
Left: Bubi and Baron
Over: Ondine
makes up
as Bubi
Next photograph:
Ondine and Mary Woronov
as Bubi: "We have
a message . . . "

NIGHT CLUB
(Bubi's Hide-Away)

Night Club was first performed by the Play-House of the Ridiculous at La MaMa Experimental Theatre Club on September 17, 1970. It was directed by John Vaccaro, with set and costume designs by Joyce and Jerry Marcel, lighting by John P. Dodd, music by The Irritations, and the following cast:

Bubi *Ondine* and *Mary Woronov*
Baron Pincus Rothschild *Gillian Lola Bercowitz*
Timmy *Hieronymus Botch*
Edwin *Bela Box*
Edwina *Herndon Ely*
Jimmy Jimmy *Otto Erotica*
Waitress *Tecquilla*
Vespucci *Charisma Penaje*
Roxanna *Christina*
Cartwright *Paul Issa*
Stampler *William G. P. Edgar*
Ten Hat Salonicus *Joe Peroni*
Shigushitsume *Penny Arcade*
Kirizuzu *Marsha Dimes*
Shigushitsuke *William G. P. Edgar*
Kazuko *Kevin Bradigan*
Taganaka *Marie Antoinette*
Young Man *Kevin Bradigan*
Young Girl *Sylvie Papernik*

This production subsequently played at the New Loft Theatre. The section of the script involving Boogie Woogie and the Tar Babies was omitted in performance, and a song, "The Third World," by Tecquilla, was interpolated.

CHARACTERS

BUBI, master of ceremonies at Bubi's Hide-Away
BARON PINCUS ROTHSCHILD, sponsor of Bubi's Hide-Away
EDWIN, ventriloquist
EDWINA, his live dummy
JIMMY JIMMY, juggler
TEN HAT SALONICUS, impersonator
COUSIN JUNIPER (optional)
THE GRAND KABUKI THEATER OF AMERICA:
SHIGUSHITSUME, a college girl
SHIGUSHITSUKE, a college boy
KIRIZUZU, girl friend to Shigushitsume
TAGANAKA, the boy's mother
KAZUKO, the girl's father
BOOGIE WOOGIE, black singer
THE TAR BABIES, Boogie's choral group
WAITRESS
TIMMY, lighting technician in drag
YOUNG MAN
YOUNG WOMAN
MUSICIANS
STAGE AUDIENCE
VICE SQUAD

Lights down. The stage and theater are dark. A VOICE *announces: "Ladies and gentlemen—Night Club!" Lively night club music, which is soon drowned out by the sound of bulldozers and jackhammers, which, along with the sounds of marching, vast crowds cheering, and an occasional explosion, will recur throughout the play. A few aborted flashes of light. Applause, catcalls, heckling, etc., from the stage* AUDIENCE. *These sounds continue as* BUBI, *the master of ceremonies, speaks to allay their impatience.*

BUBI *(Intimately, in a voice that defies sexual identification)* Hello, all you darlings out there. Don't let the darkness frighten you.

Let your hands wander a little. Have fun. This is your beloved Bubi again, bringing you yet another all-star show from Bubi's Hide-Away, your sleepy-time place, your home away from home. . . . We seem to have a slight electrical problem—*total darkness. (Laughs smoothly)* Are we going to have light, Timmy? . . . *Timmy?* . . . We may have a personnel problem, too. . . . Timmy? . . . Timmy's a little deaf. . . . No, really. He got hit in both ears by a baseball when he was a kid. He's very accident prone.

Sparks from the control booth.

Well, at least we know he's there. . . . *Timmy?* Timmy, are you alive?

A spot comes on briefly and moves erratically around the theater audience.

Well, it's progress anyway. . . . *(To someone in the audience as the spot hits him or her)* Oh, you're gorgeous, sweetheart. Meet me after the show and we'll make piggy.

The spot moves on, then fades.

Shall I entertain you with a few tales from my sordid past while we're waiting? My sins and omissions? . . . But what will I do later, then?

AUDIENCE Strip! Strip, Bubi!

BUBI *(Laughing smoothly)* You really want me to reveal all? *Everything? Tous mes secrets intimes?* . . . Darlings, the world isn't ready for it yet, believe me. It really is sordid. Much worse than getting hit in both ears with a baseball. It was a double play. Timmy's the only transvestite in the Electrician's and Stagehand's Union. He's stage struck. *(Shouting) Timmy, what the fuck are you doing in there?*

An immediate spot on BUBI, *holding his microphone. Fanfare.* BUBI *is tall and strong-looking. Although his sex is indeterminate, his sexuality is clear and strong.* HE *is strikingly made up as a woman, but dressed in a tuxedo. Muscles bulge underneath. His appearance has nothing of the homosexual; rather, it reflects strangeness and mystery. At different times* HE *is intimate, loving, heroic, remote, menacing.*

Well, now. That's a bit better. *Isn't it?*

AUDIENCE Bubi! Bubi! Bubi!

Drums, as BUBI *throws kisses, bumps and grinds a little. There is a very special quality to the* AUDIENCE*'s cries of "Bubi!" Sometimes it is merely lewd and playful, but more often it is strained, drawn out, imploring. It reflects dependency and desperation, sometimes anxiety and fear. It is ritualistic and incantatory, as if the sound itself held magical properties. Thus it is a sound that comes out of their entire being and reflects more than anything else the nature of their intricate, intimate, tormented relationship with* BUBI.

BUBI Thanks, dolls. I love you all. And you know I mean it, every last motherfucking one of you. . . . *(Laughs, as if at stupid children)* Do you all know about the cover charge? I want to warn you about the cover charge. —But hey, listen, kids, we've got a great, *simply great,* show lined up for you tonight and I do mean *stupendous.* . . . If Timmy can stop fussing with his drag and give us more light. *(Raising his voice)* Yes, *Timmy darling,* I said *light.*

AUDIENCE Strip, Bubi! Strip!

Drums. BUBI *does a few bumps and grinds.*

BUBI You know you're a filthy audience? *Reeking.* I can't see you, but I know you gotta be real filthy. . . . *And do I love it.*

Whistles. Cheers.

AUDIENCE Bubi! Bubi!

BUBI Listen, not to change the subject, I visited my mother the other day. You know, my *mère.* —A little French up the ass never hurt, huh? But you've got to watch it once you cross the border. *Schwein* everywhere.

AUDIENCE *(Delighted)* Strip, Bubi.

BUBI Come on, now. Be serious. My mother's *eighty-six.* No, I'm not kidding. I was conceived in a cornfield in her late middle years. —A grand old lady from the old school.

AUDIENCE Strip Bubi's mother! . . . Strip Bubi's mother's teacher!

BUBI *(Archly)* Have you no shame? Is nothing sacred? Did you never nurse at a mother's breast? *Any* mother? If you don't behave, I'll sing "The Star-Spangled Banner." *(Silence)* Or recite the Gettysburg Address. *(Silence)* Well now, that's much better. It's 9 Great Jones Street, in case you're interested. Later, if you're nice, we'll all suck tittie with our tea. It's a custom I learned in England. I studied at Oxford, you know. —Ah, how I miss riding to hound.

AUDIENCE Woof! Woof! Woof! Virginia! Woof! Woof!

BUBI Oh, you're all so terribly a-cultural. Excruciatingly *lumpen.* Have you never traveled? Have you never broadened your minds? Do you know that it is a respected Arab custom to blow into a camel's sexual passage to encourage it to drop its milk? . . . *(Peering)* No, no, she's not a camel, darling. Your efforts are entirely wasted on her. . . . If it's milk you want, that is.

AUDIENCE Bubi! Bubi! Bubi!

BUBI Now, where were we? Oh, yes, my *mother.*

AUDIENCE Keep it clean, Bubi.

BUBI *Cad.* I really don't know why I reveal myself to you. I mean, I simply don't have any sense of privacy.

AUDIENCE Strip Bubi's mother!

BUBI *(Coldly)* Oh, really now. You don't want to be a boor, do you? I mean, manners do still count for *something,* don't they? *(Silence)* Oh, now you're hurt. *Bad Bubi.* I'm sure you're really very sweet. *(Mocks sweetly)* Do you forgive Bubi? If you don't, I'll *cry.*

AUDIENCE Okay. But don't let it happen again.

Applause. Fanfare. Whistling.

BUBI Thanks, doll. You're one in a million. Drop dead soon, won't you?

Laughter. Lights suddenly on stage. Cheers. Whistles. BUBI *bumps and grinds briefly. Bubi's Hide-Away is a small, subterranean room. There are no windows, its outer perimeter is dark. The stage is small, the audience is jammed together, very close to the stage. The entire club is no more than ten or twelve feet across. Occasionally plaster drops from above. The club seems very vulnerable to the construction noises outside and above.*

Timmy, you beautiful beast, you've done it!

Music, while BUBI *dances quickly through his audience.*

Darlings! Light! Light! We've been reprieved. Hallelujah! *(Singing à la Hildegarde)* Darlings, *je vous aime beaucoup. . . . (He hums the rest and returns to the stage. Then, dramatically, stop-*

ping the music and noise with a wave of his arm) Le drame se commence!

Drum roll. Lights down to a spot on BUBI, *reciting excitedly from Racine's* PHEDRE, *III, 2, 813–822:*

O toi, qui vois la honte où je suis descendue,
Implacable Vénus, suis-je assez confondue?
Tu ne saurais plus loin pousser ta cruauté.
Ton triomphe est parfait; tous tes traits ont porté.
Cruelle, si tu veux une gloire nouvelle,
Attaque un ennemi qui te soit plus rebelle.
Hippolyte te fuit; et bravant ton courroux,
Jamais à tes autels n'a fléchi les genoux.
Ton nom semble offenser ses superbes oreilles.
Déesse, venge-toi: nos causes sont pareilles.*

Cheers. Whistles. Lights up. BUBI *throws kisses, then silences them suddenly with another wave of his arm.*

I don't *ever* want you to think your Bubi is illiterate.

Silence.

You may applaud.

Cheers. Whistles.

AUDIENCE Strip, Bubi! Bubi! Strip, Bubi!

BUBI Later, darlings, later. I like to keep you in suspense. It's a lover's first rule. —And we *are* lovers, aren't we?

AUDIENCE *(With great devotion)* Bubi! Bubi! Bubi!

*A translation will be found on page 54.

BUBI Thank you, thank you, my little chicks. My heart is yours forever.

AUDIENCE Bubi! Bubi!

BUBI *silences them with a gesture.*

BUBI *(Softly, sweetly, nevertheless with threat) Sweethearts . . . later.* Later we shall love and comfort. *(Whispering) Later. . . . (Raising his voice)* But right now, let's . . . *get on with the show! (He laughs. Fanfare)* But first—a word from our beloved sponsor, that man behind the man behind the scenes—

The lights flicker, as if failing.

Easy, Timmy—the owner and sole supporter of Bubi's Hide-Away—*Baron Pincus Rothschild!*

Fanfare. A short, fat man, elegantly dressed, comes on stage. Applause, cheers . BUBI *silences the audience. The* BARON *speaks enthusiastically but more or less incoherently in a stuttering German accent.*

BARON It is great pleasure to being here. Again you are all welcome to me, your host. I mean, my Bubi is one big showman . . . so you don't never mind, ha ha. Anyway, so I don't apologize here and now. It is a great moment we are having our third year and I am going broke. *I love everybody.* I am into every show girl and thing and *I love everybody!* My lawyer he is getting on rug every time his secretary without brassiere from Vassar College. My mother she is dying with blood cells but *she loves everybody!* She pinches your bottom. *(*HE *laughs, slaps* BUBI *on the back)* Bubi, you are one terrific good kid. Money— *(*HE *laughs; he cannot control it)* Go onward with show! I am going fast broke but *I love everybody! (Hugging* BUBI*, crying)* Bubi, you are killing one good Jew kid.

HE *walks off, crying. Applause, cheers. A* WAITRESS *enters with drinks on a tray. The* AUDIENCE *feels and fondles her, as* THEY *usually do when* SHE *serves. Sometimes* THEY *are quite rough with her, playing practical jokes, e.g., pouring ketchup on her, shaking soda bottles and squirting them between her legs, pouring drinks in her panties. How often* SHE *appears depends on the needs of the* AUDIENCE, *which may vary from night to night.*

BUBI Now there is a truly angelic man. Just *entre nous* he used to be my father until we became lovers. Now he is my son, and I don't know what I'm going to do with him. —But let me not burden you with my problems—

AUDIENCE Strip, Bubi! Strip!

BUBI You'd love that, wouldn't you?

Marching, gunfire above and outside. THEY *all listen.*

AUDIENCE *(Crying)* Bubi! Bubi!

BUBI *(With disdain)* You mice! All right, all right. *(Puts a smile on his face)* Yes, I'll do what I can. But I warn you . . . it's hopeless.

Silence.

(In a mincing voice) Please stop the bang-bang up there? *(*HE *laughs demonically at the* AUDIENCE. *Then, sudden silence)*—And now for the lighter side of our show. Yes! *(Making a pitch)* We are most fortunate tonight, my friends and neighbors, to have *in our audience* one of the greatest acts in show biz, an act that has stupefied, shocked, and amazed audiences on all the seven continents of this world, an act that has defied the imagination, the intelligence, and the wit of countless millions of people of all races, colors, and creeds—I mean none other than —ladies and gentlemen, I give you—*Edwin and Edwina!*

Wild cheering, cup-banging. EDWIN, *a ventriloquist, comes up from the* AUDIENCE, *dragging* EDWINA, *his live dummy.* HE *seats her on his knee, kisses* BUBI. EDWINA *falls onto* BUBI *and kisses him also.* EDWIN *slaps her. As* HE *speaks with* BUBI, EDWINA *mugs at the audience.*

EDWIN She's sex crazy. Do you hear me? She's *sex crazy.* Last week a redheaded woodpecker got to her and she had to have an abortion. I'm a ventriloquist, not a carpenter, damn it.

BUBI Why don't you keep her in mothballs, darling?

EDWIN She eats them. I tell you, she's *sex crazy.* She loves all sports with long appendages—golf, bowling, archery, knightly tournament, and harpooning. Need I say more?

BUBI She sounds very outgoing.

EDWIN Outgoing, ingoing, it's all the same to her. I tell you she's *sex crazy. (To* EDWINA*)* Right, baby? *(No response.* HE *slaps her)* Speak up, you woodhead!

EDWINA Fuuuck!

EDWIN *(Slapping her)* Don't be dirty. Tell the folks about yourself. Tell them about your childhood years when you were just a little sapling, ha ha ha.

EDWINA *(Puffing up and preparing)* Fuuuck!

EDWIN *(Slapping her)* I told you not to be dirty. I told you we're turning over a new leaf. She's been impossible since she started sapping. Edwina, what did that woodpecker do to you? *(*HE *covers her mouth before* SHE *can answer)* Never mind. Tell the folks about school. *(No response.* EDWINA *is still on "fuck."* HE *shakes her)* Edwina, tell the folks about your teacher, Mrs. Peach, ha ha, what a name, what an old maid, what a stupid old cunt. *(*HE *puts his hand in her crotch)* Edwina, tell the folks—

EDWINA *(Slapping his hand away)* Get your hand out of my pussy, you freak!

EDWIN Listen, Edwina, baby, you can be replaced by plastic. Believe me, I don't need the aggravation of woodpeckers in my house.

EDWINA *(Putting her hand in his crotch)* Fuuuck!

EDWIN *(Slapping her hand away)* Would you believe her pussy's full of termites?

BUBI But Edwin, darling, why don't you spray her?

EDWINA *(Sarcastically)* Hah!

EDWIN What does that mean? Speak up, you twig. I asked you what that means.

EDWINA You know damn well what it means.

EDWIN No, I don't know what that means. I want you to tell me what it means.

EDWINA It means you got a wooden pecker, that's what it means.

EDWIN What? Ha ha, that's a laugh. How can I have a wooden pecker? I'm flesh and—

EDWINA It never moves! *(SHE cracks up laughing over her joke)* Haaaaaaaaaaaaa!

EDWIN *(Slapping her)* Listen, I want you to be polite. *(Slapping her again)* Respectful. *(Still again)* Patriotic.

EDWINA *is stubbornly silent.*

I'm sorry if I hurt your feelings. *(No response)* I didn't mean to hit you so hard. *(No response.* HE *puts his hand in her crotch)* Edwina, say something.

EDWINDA *(Smiling slowly)* Haaaaaaaaa!

EDWIN Edwina!

EDWINA Fuuuck!

EDWIN Edwina!

EDWINA *drags him struggling to the floor in an embrace. Fanfare, applause. Cheers.*

BUBI *(Clapping)* Aren't they terrific? Give them a hand, folks. Eddie, come on up here.

EDWIN *comes to the microphone,* EDWINA *slung over his shoulder.*

Edwin, you were delightful. It's lovely to have you back. Tell us, how long did it take you to perfect your act?

EDWIN Well, Bubi, with the whittling and all—

EDWINA Hah!

EDWIN *(Patting* EDWINA*'s backside)* and her low IQ—

EDWINA Get your finger outa my anal passage!

EDWIN *cracks up laughing. Fanfare.* EDWIN *and* EDWINA *retire behind* BUBI, EDWIN *smiling and waving,* EDWINA *mugging wildly.*

BUBI

As the applause subsides.

Great kids. And a great act. Not many people know that Edwin started out from Akron, Ohio.

Scattered cheers from AUDIENCE.

Edwin had polio when he was ten, but he's made a courageous comeback. What do you think about that, kids?

Scattered cheers.

He is also the sole support of his widowed mother.

Silence.

AUDIENCE Strip Edwin's mother! . . . Strip Edwin's dummy! . . . *Fuck* Edwin's dummy!

EDWINA Oh, yeah? You bet yer ass. *Anytime.* But you better be good, buddy.

Scattered cackles.

AUDIENCE *(Falsetto, teasing) Edwina!*

EDWINA Bubi, you androgynous fuck, shut their mouths up before I fire you.

Catcalls, whoops.

BUBI Sweetheart, you shouldn't use words you can't spell.

EDWINA Oh, yeah? F-U-C-K! Androgynous *fuck!*

Whoops, cackles. Fanfare.

BUBI Well, kiddies, I see we're off again to a swell start. I really didn't think we'd make it tonight. Our lease has expired, Timmy's very flippy, the Baron has lost his marbles, and the press thinks we're terribly degenerate. *Our entire chorus line is menstruating,* and the vice squad is due any minute.

AUDIENCE Bubi! Strip, Bubi!

Drums. BUBI *bumps and grinds.*

BUBI Oh, you naughty children. Just for that I'm going to give you a little moral uplift. Give me a spot, Timmy. *(Nothing happens) Timmy!*

Lights down to a single spot on BUBI, *holding the microphone close.*

Those ears will be the death of me. —Hello, hello. This is Bubi calling from Bubi's Hide-Away. Do you read me? We are all present and accounted for. We are all present and accounted for. Do you read me? Do you read me? We have buried our dead and suckled the newborn, but the situation is desperate. Large insects are eating away at our walls. The lights are uncertain, our food supply is unpredictable. In the streets, our words are not understood and we are pursued, beaten, and killed. We have nowhere to turn. Repeat: *we have nowhere to turn.* Over. Over.

Static, then the sounds of bulldozers and jackhammers.

AUDIENCE *(Frightened)* Bubi! Bubi! Bubi!

BUBI *(Flippantly)* You'll have to trust me, kids. We androgynites are a tricky bunch.

AUDIENCE Bubi!

EDWINA *(Mocking)* Bubi!

Lights up, as BUBI *does a few more bumps and grinds.*

BUBI Can it, kids. In the immortal words of the Baron, *ve go onvard vit show!*

Cheers, whistles, etc.

Friends, I'm so very proud and pleased to have in our audience tonight, direct from Newark, New Jersey—

Cheers, whistles.

I see we have a lot of New Jerseyites here.

AUDIENCE Denver, Colorado! Kleenex, Nebraska! Baton Rouge, Louisiana! Syphilis, Wyoming! —Syphilis, D. C.

BUBI Well, we have at least a *few* New Jerseyites. Does New Jersey have an anthem? What?

AUDIENCE "Secaucus, Forever."

BUBI "Secaucus, Forever?" You must sing it for us some night. — No, *not tonight. Some* night. You Jersey people are pretty stupid, aren't you? I mean, you're lovely, but *stupid.* —Listen, if we can cut the small talk I'll gladly get to our next act, and believe me, this guy is sensational, with a capital "L."

AUDIENCE *Go onvard vit show! (Cheers, whistles, etc.)*

BUBI *(Barking)* Hiya, hiya, hiya, folks. Gather ye 'round and listen to our next startling attraction direct from Newark—

Cheers, whistles.

New *Joisey.* We have here, in the flesh, in the living, breathing, succulent flesh, that favorite of child and adult alike, that magnificent master of gratuitous gravity, the levitational and lighthearted wizard of the western world—Jimmy *(Pause) Jimmy!*

Cheers, etc.

Here he is, folks, let's give Jimmy Jimmy a hand.

JIMMY Bubi, you don't look a day over fifty.

Laughs from AUDIENCE.

How do you do it?

BUBI Yogurt, darling, lots and lots of yogurt. Are you still impotent?

Laughs, hoots from AUDIENCE.

JIMMY *(Getting right into it)* Folks, I hold here a simple piece of rope, no more, no less. Call it a string and you would be wrong. Call it a hawser and you would be equally wrong. Just a simple ordinary piece of rope, of exactly twenty-four inches in length and one inch in diameter, useful for a hundred and one household purposes. I can twist it, swing it, tie it into knots, and even chew it, if I wish. It is conceivable that I could swallow it, and it has been known among the famous yogi of India and Afghanistan to insert it into the rectum up to the length of forty-nine feet and have it come out the oral orifice. Let me say at once that I am not one of these famous yogi. I cannot raise weights with my penis nor can I retrieve my sperm once it has been expended, may it rest in peace. If I hold this piece of rope vertically and release the bottommost end, it dangles. If I hold this piece of rope vertically and release the topmost end, it falls, as you can all see. Therefore *(Tossing the rope away)* I engage in no rope tricks of any sort, manner or kind. I am not a charlatan, I am not an impostor, I am not a trickster of any kind. Whatever I do before your eyes will be the result not of deception, not of devotion to foreign ideologies, not of any alliance with the forces of darkness, but of pure and simple skill learned at my father's knee, a skill to which I, as did my father and his fathers before him, have devoted my life and many long hours to acquiring. *(Snapping his fingers)* Pedro!

The BARON, *looking furtive and disheveled in a large Mexican sombrero, wheels in a cart with crockery.* JIMMY *prepares himself, e.g. exercises.*

BARON *(To* BUBI*)* Psst! Psst!

BUBI Why, Pedro, how you've changed.

BARON Bah! Don't you are seeing it is I the Baron is here?

BUBI Pedro, your Spanish is deteriorating.

BARON *Mister Bubi! Please!* You are listening to me now in big danger. I am messed up by *vice-squad men* who are screwing up chorus girls all in row. —Don't you are hearing me? They are stuck down like carrots *all in row!*

BUBI Darling, it's their training, you know.

BARON *Bubi!* I am screaming to them I am one good Jew kid, but they are throwing me down and giving me *one big screw!*

BUBI Well, you obviously can't complain about them to the Anti-Defamation League.

BARON *Bubi!* They are *exporting* me, I who am screwing everybody *but not in row. (Screaming) I love everybody! You are killing me, Bubi, one good Jew!*

BUBI *(Bored)* Pedro, please peddle your pecker elsewhere. I'm not your Queen of the May.

BARON *Bubi!*

JIMMY And now folks, with limber joint and nimble knuckle, we get to the meat of our demonstration. But first—Pedro!—a little family tradition.

The BARON *puts on a metal helmet.*

In my family, it is always said before we perform, if you break an egg you get an omelette. So—

He breaks a dish over the helmet, and the BARON *wanders off in a daze.*

on with the show!

Fanfare, cheers, etc.

Now, folks, I know you've seen jugglers before. You've seen jugglers juggle balls, you've seen jugglers juggle Indian clubs, you've seen jugglers juggle dishes. Now, folks, I confess to being a juggler and to being a juggler of dishes, but *there* any similarity ends. All jugglers of dishes juggle dishes of uniform weight, size, and price. Is that not so? Am I not correct? Don't be afraid to speak up, it's a free country. —And I say to you that that is boring, cowardly, and in bad taste. Why must there be such uniformity? Why must there be such a lack of imagination? Why must there be so little challenge to the laws of mother nature? And so you see here before you tonight, folks, this genuine Majolica dishware from the fourteenth century of sunny Italy valued at $2600, this saucer of the finest Wedgewood from our friendly England across the sea valued at $300, this Sèvres cup from the frog capital of the world, the land of perfume, French fries, and performing ladies, valued, ladies and gentlemen, at $1400, and finally but not least, this early American gravy bowl with a portrait of our first president on the bottom inside, rough-hewn and common, it is true, and I never would deny it, but—BUT . . . inscribed with the *handwriting* of our one and only forefather, the great, the revered, the inspiring G. Wash.—that is G. Washington, folks, *I kid you not!*—valued at, valued at, valued at—can we even *place* a value on so unique and incredible an article of art and history? Nevertheless, I tell you, and you can believe my words, folks, that I know a man, a gentleman of the highest order, who would give me $50,000 cash *today* in small used denominations to possess this object for his very own to fondle and touch. —Ladies and gentlemen, *that* is the kind of juggler I am!

Wild cheers, etc.

And now for the proof of the pudding, the sauce that gilds the goose, folks—*the act itself!*

Drum roll, finger flexes, etc. HE *steps back, spaces out the crockery, crouches, balances, and then quickly, one after another, throws all four objects in the air.* HE *misses every one. They break. There is a stunned silence.*

(Proudly) Ladies and gentlemen, I give you—a $54,300 omelette!

BUBI Beautiful, baby. Beautiful.

Fanfare. Wild cheers, etc.

Jimmy. Jimmy Jimmy, come here, you wild man. *(Hugging him)* Jimmy, you're fantastic. Tell me, how did you ever create such a stupendous act? Where did you ever get the balls?

JIMMY Well, Bubi—gee, you've really aged—you see, for years I was just doing the same old junk, throwing up and catching and throwing up again. And then one day, well, like it hit me. I said to myself, why do you have to catch them? Where is it written? And that was it. It was like a whole new ball game. I just added a few touches, refined here and there, and *voilà,* there it was.

Fanfare, cheers as JIMMY *retreats behind* BUBI.

BUBI Beautiful. Beautiful. That kid is going places. *Absolutely.*

Waving a message, the WAITRESS *enters through the crowd.*

The night club acts: Jimmy Jimmy; Edwin, Edwina
Over:
Timmy and Bubi

It seems we have a message. . . . Let the dumpling through, please. *Sweethearts, a message.*

Gradual quiet. Lights down to a single spot on BUBI. *Heavy marching outside and above.* BUBI *reads to himself.*

It is not a happy message. I don't think I should read it.

AUDIENCE Read it, Bubi! Read it!

BUBI I tell you it is not a happy message.

AUDIENCE No, Bubi. No! No!

BUBI Yes. Yes, it's true. Some of our dearest and oldest friends are no longer here. Others are mutilated. Look around you at the missing fingers, the missing arms and legs. *Cancer* is rampant. Eyeballs rest precariously in their sockets. Hearts beat fainter and fainter. *Our burdens are too heavy* . . . and we bend, bend into sickness and despair. *(Shouting desperately) Where is our joy?*

AUDIENCE *(Whimpering)* Bubi. Bubi.

BUBI *(Subdued)* These, then, are our latest casualties: *Vespucci*, of the laughing eyes. Testicles . . . crushed, wax in his nose and honey in his ears. He neither hears nor makes love. Each day, blood in his urine. When his mouth opens to speak, to ask medical aid, they break his teeth with a hammer.
Roxanna, who loved men. Macrocephalia and withered arms. She cannot embrace. Discharge of all her bodily fluids. Her brains have turned to jelly, and in her deepest recesses, dead fish. Where are you, beautiful Roxanna, whose walk made men passionate on summer afternoons? *(Whispering fiercely)* Where are you?
Cartwright, whose mind saw into all things. All day now, he picks wonders from his nose. Coprostasis and silence. Eyes in-

tense but suppurating. Skin: *Streptococculatus erysipela.* Cartwright, who above all had courage to live, lacks now the courage to die. Treatment: hot irons up the rectum, gouging of the eyes, and peeling of the skin. If no response, acute strangulation. Prognosis: *unfavorable.*

And *Stampler,* of the beautiful body and beautiful voice. His chords have been ripped out and all appendages cut. He still whispers, but there is no one to hear him. Once each week when the sun is at its height, they parade beautiful women naked before him on the lawn. He cannot touch them. And when he tries to lick them, they put fishhooks through his tongue. At any moment they will pull him in, singing hymns. We shall not hear his screams. They are trapped within him.

Silence. The WAITRESS *leaves quickly, unmolested.*

AUDIENCE Bubi! Bubi! Save us!

Scattered weeping, pounding of fists on tables.

BUBI *(Laughing scornfully)* Save you? For what? For what? When you leave here tonight, if you dare, three more of you will go. They are waiting. It is the week of boiling things. Your heads shall bob with parsnips in pots of gold.

AUDIENCE No, Bubi! No!

BUBI *(Laughing) Yes. Yes.* Bubi cannot save you. Bubi can only *(Pause) entertain* you. *(He laughs again)*

AUDIENCE Strip, Bubi! Strip, Bubi!

Fanfare. BUBI *bumps and grinds briefly.*

BUBI Oh, you filthy little darlings. I fuck you all. Do you *hear? All.*

AUDIENCE Bubi! Bubi! Bubi!

The BARON *rushes in in tatters, kneels and clutches at* BUBI.

BARON Bubi! You are helping me! I am for Jesus Christ one hot baby with vice coppers on my back all in row I am screwing and *(Howling) I love everybody!*

BUBI That's lovely, Baron. I hope you're not hurting anyone.

BARON *(Desperately)* Bubi!

BUBI *(Pushing him gently away with his foot)* Baron, if it will make it any easier for you, there is a cock for every dawn, and in the course of time we are all violated, *violated*, VIOLATED! Do you understand? You ask me to save you. From *what? Who* will save *me?* Do you not see me withering before your eyes? What do you know of my pain? Do you know that I am a hundred years old, possibly even three thousand years old? Baron, listen to me, find yourself a window, break the glass, rub your arm along the jagged edge, and scream for help. I assure you *(Laughs) no one will come.* Baron, go back to your girls *(Imitating) all in row.* Finish your scream.

The BARON *stares at him wildly a few seconds, then scrambles off in confusion on all fours, stopping several times to open his mouth, as if to scream. There is no sound.*

(Flippantly) I *worry* about that boy. I really do. . . . *(With a throaty chuckle)* But let me introduce you now to a boy I *don't* worry about, *everybody's favorite greasy Greek, Ten Hat Salonicus*!

Fanfare. TEN HAT SALONICUS *comes to the stage. He is a big beefy type.*

Ten Hat, welcome back. The last time I saw you you were only Seven Hat Salonicus. *Wha happa?*

TEN HAT Well . . . I got married. Whataya think? That made for three more hats.

BUBI I see. Your wife wears many hats.

TEN HAT No. She don't wear none.

BUBI I don't understand. Perhaps you'd better speak Greek.

TEN HAT I only speak Italian.

BUBI Why is that?

TEN HAT *(Laughing)* The same reason, dolly. She fucks.

BUBI Ten Hat, *who* fucks?

TEN HAT My *wife*, stupid. Don't you know why I'm Ten Hat now?

BUBI But of course. And she fucks in Italian, so you don't speak Greek.

TEN HAT Dat's right! You got the whole fucking thing! Somewhere you got a brain. Maybe up your ass, huh? Ha ha ha!

BUBI Tell me, Ten Hat, do you envisage ever becoming Twelve Hat or even Twenty or Sixty Hat Salonicus?

TEN HAT *(Offended)* You knocking my wife, mister? I don't play around.

BUBI I beg your pardon, Ten Hat?

TEN HAT Ah, that's better. I don't let nobody knock my wife. She's a real apple of my eye.

BUBI Indeed.

TEN HAT She's a *sweetheart.*

BUBI I'm sure she is.

TEN HAT What's the matter, you don't like small talk? You in a hurry or something? Listen, I been a pro ever since I was Two Hat, and I'm telling you the small talk is good for my act. The audience laps it up like a bunch of cocksuckers. It puts them in the mood. You know, for example, what my wife does in bed? Huh?

BUBI I'm afraid to ask. *(Pause)* What?

TEN HAT She *fucks.* How's dat for character?

BUBI *(After a pause)* I think, Ten Hat, the audience is as much in the mood as they'll ever be.

TEN HAT You bet your ass they are, Bubi. I'm gonna do my United States southern belle first, okay?

BUBI *(Imitating)* You bet your ass, Ten Hat.

TEN HAT *(Laughing)* Now you got the spirit. Hey, Bubi, you ever fuck?

BUBI Only southern belles, Ten Hat.

TEN HAT *(Laughing)* Hey, you got a sense of humor, too. You must be Greek. Okay. Here's your southern belle. *(*HE *puts on a wig and a southern belle hat. In this impersonation* HE *is hopelessly inept. Before* HE *speaks,* HE *primps and postures)* Oh, ah do declare, ah is in a *state.* Ah simply is in bad need of a sound fuck. The field hands is all picking cotton, and the house hands is all members of the Urban League. Ah don't know what a poor girl is to do.

The AUDIENCE *throws bananas on the stage.*

(Picking one up) Ah do declare, it is a banana. Ah was brought up not to mess with bananas. But ah do love bananas. Bananas is the bane of mah existence. Mah daddy would be so ashamed of me if ah messed with a banana. —Oh, there is mah maternal cousin Juniper. He is a living faggot—but he is a living faggot with a living ding-dong, and ah know that a ding-dong is not a banana. Oh, Juniper. Juniper, will you come heah for a moment. Ah have a confidence to entrust to you. *(Peeling the banana archly)* Cousin, ah *loves* bananas. You know how I just *consume* bananas and how mah daddy disapproves of mah inclination. But Cousin Juniper, ah *loves* bananas, ah just *do.* And mah question to you is—will you save this poor girl from this dreadful, fascinating banana? Ah is simply perishing for bad need of a— No, Juniper. You cannot have mah banana. It is *mah* banana. It is all I have till sundown! No! Juniper! *(Eating the banana voraciously)* I will kick you in your family's jewels, Juniper! You cannot have it! It is mine! And I love bananas! —Oh! Ohhh! *(HE has an orgasm as he crams the last of the banana in his mouth)* Mah daddy would be so *ashamed* of me! *(HE whips off the hat but not the wig)*

Fanfare.

(HE clasps his hands over his head like a boxer in the ring, then puts on a hat of an officer of the Third Reich. HE makes guttural sounds in his throat, salutes, and stomps his feet in preparation) Ach! Ach! Ach! Achtung! Achtung! Testing, testing, testing, achtung! Achchoo! *(With a German accent)* People of the Third Reich, we are here to give our support to our beloved leader!

Cheers.

We have arrived at our moment of destiny and we must, we will, achieve victory!

Cheers.

We must destroy our enemies! We must keep ourselves pure for the future. We must fuck into our women and make them pregnant—

AUDIENCE *Ja! Ja!*

TEN HAT —and then we must give our children a society of health, honor and strength!

Cheers.

(Saluting) We must therefore follow our great leader—

AUDIENCE *Sieg heil! Sieg heil! Sieg heil!*

THEY *continue through his speech. Marching above. Cheers from huge crowds.*

TEN HAT —into victory over our enemies. We must save the world from its own contamination and destruction! We must bring to pass a new day, a new order, a new world! *(Clutching his crotch)* The divine power Himself has sanctioned our mission. As we march onward, we march under the canopy of *(His crotch again)* divine blessing. We cannot, we must not fail. We must achieve success. And we can achieve success only through absolute obedience to our great leader—

HE *turns expectantly. The* BARON *rushes out in a frenzy.* HE *has found his scream.* HE *has on long underwear, a brassiere, and a bonnet.* HE *leaps on* TEN HAT *to strangle him, dragging him offstage.*

BARON *Schwein! Schwein! Schwein! Schwein!*

AUDIENCE *Sieg heil! Sieg heil! Sieg heil!*

Fanfare. Cheers, etc.

EDWINA Boy, what a load of shit.

BUBI Ten Hat? Ten Hat, you nefarious Greek, come out here. *(No response. To* AUDIENCE*)* Well, I assume he's Eleven Hat by now.

AUDIENCE *(Laughing)* Bubi! Bubi! Bubi!

BUBI *(Imitating Mae West)* Listen, dolls. Don't you worry about a thing. There's plenty more where that came from, and five'll get you ten you're going to get it.

AUDIENCE *(Eating it up)* Bubi! Bubi!

BUBI Yeah. Which brings me to the Grand Kabuki Theatre of Japan. You spell that K-A-B-U-K-I, they got a very foreign language over there, as well as a lot of *artistes,* you better believe it. I go for art no matter what language it's in.

AUDIENCE *(Eating it up)* Bubi! Bubi!

BUBI *(Still Mae West)* And that little digression just happens to bring me to the point of my little talk, which is that we have here with us tonight several of the leading *artistes*—I speak from personal experience—of the Grand Kabuki Theatre of *America,* yeah, you heard it right the first time, buster, *America.* I was never a fussy woman. So without any further fuss and ado, I give you—and you can have it—*The Grand Kabuki Theatre of America.*

Quick scene of pandemonium backstage at the Kabuki. STAGEHANDS *in black, rushing anonymously back and forth, attacks of temperament and nerves, props set, last touches of makeup and costume. Much Oriental noise. Then* ONE OF THEM *claps his hands and screams a speech. A large frame with a curtain is set up on* BUBI*'s stage. Cymbals clash. Drumsticks rattle on the floor as the curtain of the improvised stage is pulled across. The Kabuki* ACTORS *are dressed and made up in traditional Kabuki style.* BUBI *narrates.* The drama is in English, but the sounds are

Japanese. *Thus, it is impossible to know what the actors are saying.* THEY *may improvise with the sounds as much as they like. The drama is accompanied by a bizarre band of strings and percussion.*

BUBI *(Holding a fan to suit the occasion; in his usual voice)* The scene opens with Shigushitsume, a young college girl, sitting on the campus lawn bemoaning her fate to her college chum, Kirizuzu. She fears that she has been made pregnant by her boyfriend, Shigushitsuke, the captain of the basketball team, because she feels the seed of life growing within her.

SHIGUSHITSUME *(Pointing to her crotch with an alarmed expression)* Heeeeeeeeeeeeee sssssssssssttttttttttiiiiieeeeeeeeccccccccckkkkk mmmmmmeeeeeeeeeeeiiiiiiiii!

BUBI She says to Kirizuzu, "He stick me," meaning he has stuck me, meaning they have had sexual intercourse, the word "stick" here having the feudal connotation of some degree of force.

KIRIZUZU *(With great agitation)* Hhhhwwwwwhhhhheeeennnnn?!

BUBI Kirizuzu, who is very much the girl about campus, takes the news calmly and asks, "When?"

SHIGUSHITSUME *(Waving her hands wildly)* Eeeeeeeeeeeeeaaaaaaaaaaaaacccccchhhtttttuuuuuuuuuuzzzzzzzzz-zddddaaaaaaaaaiiiiiiieeeeeeeeee weeeeeeeeeeeeeeeeeeeeeeeek.

BUBI "Last Tuesday a week," says Shigushitsume, indicating the flight of twenty thousand crows to show . . . that the seeds of summer now await harvesting, after which will follow the barrenness of winter.

KIRIZUZU *(In a fury of sound and movement)* Sssssssssaaaaaaaaaiiiiiiiiiii lllaaaaaaaaaaaa vvveeeeeeeeeeeeee.

BUBI Kirizuzu answers her friend, "*C'est la vie.*" At this point, Shigushitsuke enters. He is wearing his robes and carrying a basketball. He is on his way to basketball practice.

SHIGUSHITSUKE Aaaaaaaaaaiiiiiiieeeeeeeeeeuuuuuuuuuuuu.

BUBI "Oh," he says, "it's you."

SHIGUSHITSUME *(Trembling, as she points between her legs)* Eeeeeeeeeeuuuuuuuuuuuuuuuuusssssttttiiiiiiiiiiiicccccckkkkkk mmmmeeeeeeeeeeeeeeeeeeeeeeee!

BUBI Trembling violently, Shigushitsume accuses him of having stuck her. Unknown to Shigushitsume, Kirizuzu is making eyes at Shigushitsuke. He is interested, but before he can respond very much, Kazuko, father of Shigushitsume and president of the local chamber of commerce, bursts upon the scene. Planting himself before Shigushitsuke, he accuses him of having stuck his daughter.

KAZUKO Uuuuuuuuuuu sssstttiiiiiicccccccckkkkkk hhhrrrrrrrrrrr!

BUBI Unseen by any of them, Taganaka, the boy's mother, has approached. She recognizes Kazuko as the father of her illegitimate son, Shigushitsuke. Unable to control herself, she accuses Kazuko of having stuck her.

TAGANAKA *(Wailing)* Uuuuuuuuuu sssttttiiiiiiiiicccccckkkkkk mmmeeeeeeeeeeeeeeeeee!

KAZUKO *(Delighted)* Eeeeeeeeeeeeeeeeaaaaaaaaaaahhhhhhhhh!

BUBI It is obvious that Kazuko is charmed to see Taganaka again after an absence of twenty years. He holds his hand tightly between his legs as in the samurai rape invocation and ejaculates an emphatic "*Yah,*" implicit in which is the intention of "sticking" her again. He makes an obscene gesture and leads her wailing into the nearby shrubbery. Kirizuzu, feeling that the ambiance is right, reveals her buttocks to Shigushitsuke, who is overwhelmed by them. Strangulated sounds issue from his throat, indicating that he is possessed by the thousand demons of passion. He staggers, gives Shigushitsume his basketball, and leads Kirizuzu into the nearby shrubbery. Shigushitsume, now alone, bewails her fate.

SHIGUSHITSUME Eeeeeeeeeeeee sssssstttttiiiiiiicccccccckkkkkk mmmmmmeeeeeeeeeeeeeeeeeeee!

BUBI She realizes that when her father seduced Shigushitsuke's mother, a curse was placed on her family and has come to pass in Shigushitsuke's sticking of her. She realizes that the only true happiness now can be for Kirizuzu and Shigushitsuke, her half-brother, to stick each other. Bravely and nobly, to the sounds of lovers in the shrubbery, she beats out her brains with the basketball, as the musicians sing the haunting lament, "He stick me."

Drumsticks on the floor. The curtain closes. Cheers, etc. The lights flicker, then go out.

Oh-oh. Hold it, sweethearts. Timmy's on the blink again.

AUDIENCE *(Desperately)* Strip, Bubi!

Heavy static, radio noises. Then a single spot on BUBI, *who is wearing earphones.*

BUBI I think we have a radio message. Yes. Yes, wait, it's getting through. *(In a monotone, repeating word by word)* Mount the battlements of dung and keep watch for the birds. The birds are now south of you. Build fires into the long night. They will come first as thunder, shattering the skies. Leave offerings. Take cover. They will chasten the land and raise up the dead. *(Static. He looks at his* AUDIENCE*)* That's it. That's all of it.

The lights come up. A few moments of silence. The band tries a feeble fanfare. The WAITRESS *serves drinks. In a sudden fury*

THEY *strip her almost completely.* SHE *manages to escape to* BUBI.

(Angrily) Oh, you fools! You fools! You poor frightened fools!

AUDIENCE *(Pleading)* Bubi! Bubi! Bubi!

BUBI Don't you know that this girl is one day to bear a child with an eagle's head? And that that head will peck out your eyes and leave you to wander forever in darkness? Who, then, will hold your hand and lead you to warmth and food if not this girl—this girl on whom you lay your greedy, desperate fingers?

AUDIENCE *(Pleading)* Bubi! Bubi! Bubi!

BUBI *(Switching suddenly in mood)* Well, I suppose we'll have to forgive them. *(Sweetly, to the* WAITRESS, *as he fondles her)* Shall we forgive them, loveliness? Ummm? They're quite incorrigible. Pissheads all, but I do love them. Come on, darling, sing us a song. *(Coaxing her onto a table)* Sing us a lullaby. Soothe our battered souls.

The WAITRESS *undulates slowly, sensuously, as the* AUDIENCE *gets worked up; e.g., "Oh, baby, baby!" "Shake it, baby!" Then* SHE *sings a lullaby, after which* SHE *runs off to wild cheering.*

BUBI *Wow.* Now, sweethearts, is that forgiving or isn't it?

AUDIENCE *(Happy again)* Bubi! Bubi! Strip, Bubi!

BUBI You realize you don't deserve a girl like that. She has a perfect body. She was made to be loved. —And she loves to be made. Her mother was a maid of all work, and her father made millions. There's "made" in every bone and muscle of her.

AUDIENCE *(Lustfully)* Bubi! Bubi!

BUBI No, no, no. You've had your chance. You'll just have to masturbate a while. Listen, when *I* was a child—

THEY *laugh. Throughout his recital* THEY *heckle.*

You don't think I was ever a child? Well, you just listen. I won't say what *kind* of child I was, but I *was* a child. I was very gentle. I picked flowers in sweet-smelling, sun-filled meadows, and my heart followed the flights of butterflies on slow summer days. I slept peacefully at night and awakened each morning joyfully. I took candy from strangers. I was a loving child. —And then I grew up.

AUDIENCE Bubi!

BUBI I came to the big city!

AUDIENCE Bubi!

BUBI The bright lights!

AUDIENCE Bubi!

BUBI I lost *all* my innocence!

AUDIENCE Bubi! Bubi!

BUBI I stopped taking candy from strangers!

AUDIENCE Bubi!

BUBI I lost hope, I despaired. I wanted to take my own life!

AUDIENCE No, Bubi, no!

BUBI And then . . . then I met the *Baron.*

Loud, brassy parade music as the BARON *comes out with a cluster of balloons.* HE *now has on a long skirt over his long underwear, but is still bare-chested with a brassiere and bonnet.*

The Baron saved me. Come here, sweetie. Let me fix you up. You're a total mess. *(He puts a wig on the* BARON, *lipstick, rouge, eye make-up)* You can't go into a police precinct looking like that. They wouldn't treat you with respect. They give you an internal, you know. In your case, they might even give you a sigmoidoscopy.

BARON Bah! Internal! They will never find me. I am remote. I am ten thousand times dead already! *(In a daze)* What are you doing to me?

BUBI Preparing you for the kill, Baron.

BARON I am confused. . . . *I love everybody* and everybody is screwing me *all in row!* Why are you messing with me? Why don't you let me die in peace? Why are you not nice to me? *I am an old man!*

BUBI Baron, can you dance?

BARON What? *(Dreaming)* Yes. Yes, I once used to dance the minuet.

BUBI *(Snapping his fingers to the* MUSICIANS*)* Boys?

THEY *play a minuet.* BUBI *and the* BARON *dance.*

There is beauty in the minuet. Measure, rhythm, expectations fulfilled, comfort.

BARON I gave you all my money.

BUBI And I gave you beauty. Girls, beautiful girls.

BARON I thought you would help me, save me.

BUBI For what? We are all dying, Baron, every moment. I love the music of Mozart above all other.

BARON Mozart was a German.

BUBI Austrian, Baron.

BARON Worse.

BUBI His music has the heartbeat of civilization.

BARON *(Laughing loudly)* Bubi, you are killing me, one good Jew.

BUBI *(Laughing)* Baron, I never meant to tell you this. I've checked the records. You're not a Jew at all. You're really a Pole. The *Russians* are killing you, not I. *(Laughs)*

BARON *(Laughing)* I was in disguise. I tried to be a gypsy, but I could not play the violin. *(Crying suddenly, as he stops dancing)* They killed them *all! All! (Indicating the heights of children with his hands) They were so small!*

BUBI Baron, you know I would save you if I could.

BARON You hate me. You take my money and you hate me.

BUBI I love you, Baron. *I love you.*

The music stops abruptly.

BARON *Then why are you killing me?*

Fanfare. The BARON *rushes out.*

BUBI What a doll. I hope he makes it. . . . Frankly, I've got my doubts. —*Meanwhile,* back on the stage at Bubi's Hide-Away, Bubi is getting ready to call to life once again that lark of the

Southland, the inimitable, the inevitable *Boogie Woogie*—and the *Tar Babies.*

Cheers, whistles.

Come up here, Boogie, you old eightball. Let's have a change of race.

BOOGIE *and the* TAR BABIES, *in blackface, come on stage.*

Now, Boogie, you can have watermelon later and shine my shoes, but right now I want you to show the folks that you got rhythm. You understand?

BOOGIE *(Rolling his eyes)* Yes, sir!

Every time BOOGIE *speaks, the* TAR BABIES *give each other some skin and grin broadly.*

BUBI You keep your big black rapist dick in its cradle, hear?

BOOGIE *laughs.*

By the way, how are all the little Woogies, picking cotton with their mammy?

BOOGIE *laughs.*

You know, you have beautiful teeth. And really, very attractive hair.

BOOGIE *laughs.*

What are you going to sing tonight, *boy?*

BOOGIE Ah got a new hymn I wants to sing.

BUBI A hymn? What kind of hymn?

BOOGIE It's a hymn about all the gladness in my heart. It's called "You Got to Fuck Jesus."

BUBI I see. "You Got to Fuck Jesus."

BOOGIE Yes, sir.

BUBI Well, it's a thought, anyway.

BOOGIE Yes, *sir!*

BUBI Hit it, Boogie!

Accompaniment: tambourine, drums, piano or guitar. A slow, heavy rhythm. After each line, the TAR BABIES *sing the chorus, "Who-wah, who-wah-wah."*

BOOGIE *(Sings)*

Je-e-sus love you.
He give you his all.
You got to repay him.
You all got to ball.
You got to fuck Jesus
Cause Jesus love you.

Je-e-sus love you.
He go down for you.
So you got to go down
And do what you do.
You got to fuck Jesus
Cause Jesus love you!

Je-e-sus love you.
They all call him dead.
So give him a hard-on.

Jump into your bed.
You got to fuck Jesus
Cause Jesus love you!

Je-e-sus love you.
He love all the way.
So take out your pussy.
It's come time to pay.
You got to fuck Jesus
Cause Jesus love you!

TEN HAT *(Coming forward in his wig and southern belle hat)* Come on, boy, it's mint julep time!

HE *leads* BOOGIE *away. Cheers, applause.*

BUBI There's a lot of white in that boy.

Explosions outside.

Sweethearts, they're getting closer. Very and much. Do you want to try making contact again?

AUDIENCE Bubi! Bubi!

BUBI Anything for you, darlings. Lights, Timmy! Give me atmosphere.

After a moment or two TIMMY *appears suddenly, in full drag, an electrician's belt with tools around his waist.* HE *wears huge hearing aids.*

TIMMY You really want atmosphere, baby?

BUBI Timmy, you're breaking the dramatic unities.

TIMMY Baby, I got my own unities to worry about.

BUBI Timmy, you look *divine.*

TIMMY I *am* divine.

BUBI You make me feel like tearing off a piece of ass.

TIMMY Darling, it would ruin my mascara.

TEN HAT Hey, dolink, you got a ding-dong maybe?

EDWINA Yeah, you got a woodpecker, you minion of Sappho?

TIMMY Bubele, *who* are these unwashed types you're catering to now?

THEY *laugh jeeringly at* TIMMY.

I don't think I like them.

THEY *laugh again.*

So crude.

THEY *laugh again.*

Bubi, I really think I must leave.

BUBI Timmy, I hear you were involved in a little abortion recently.

TIMMY Darling, I'm positively prostate. The union feels I'm bad for their image. Isn't that a laugh? *(Seductively)* They're applying all kinds of pressure.

BUBI Oh, darling, horrible. What are you doing about it?

TIMMY *(Making a grand exit)* Darling, didn't you know? I *own* the union, every swinging dickeyboy of them.

Catcalls and whistles after TIMMY, *who throws kisses back.*

BUBI Isn't she a peach?

EDWINA She's a douche bag if a day.

TIMMY *(Turning suddenly)* And you, dearie, you're a *stupid fuck!*

HE *flounces out to jeers and hoots.*

BUBI Now, now, now, don't be nasty, darlings. We've still got a long night ahead of us. We *need* Timmy.

The lights dim to just a spot on BUBI. *It is too bright, and* BUBI *squints.*

Timmy. Timmy, behave yourself. I had nothing to do with it. . . . Timmy, you're *beautiful. Please?*

The light dims to normal.

Thank you, Timmy. I love you a million kisses. *(To* AUDIENCE*)* Sweethearts, I can't see you too well, but can you put me in the mood a little? I feel . . . a little disconcerted, possibly even diseased. And I'm so, so sad.

AUDIENCE Bubi! Strip, Bubi! —Bubele!

EDWINA Show us your tit, Bubi!

Drums. BUBI *bumps and grinds briefly.*

BUBI *(Laughing)* Oh, I love it, I love it. I feel better already. You're so dependable.

AUDIENCE *(Eating it up)* Bubi! Bubi!

BUBI *(He blows into the microphone a few times. There is a brief pronounced silence, then, speaking intimately)* Hello, out there. Hello, out there. This is Bubi calling again, Bubi, from Bubi's Hide-Away. We are in deep anxiety about our future. Our walls are crumbling, we have no resistance. We have no place to go. We cannot come out. You are welcome to our wealth, to our bodies. We shall give all manner of pleasure and delight. But do not destroy us, do not destroy us. Leave us our souls. We are flesh, we are naked, we are helpless. We live, we breathe. We are gathered here, in this hole, Bubi's Hide-Away, our last retreat, to give succor and solace to each other. Our eyes are big with fear and waiting. We no longer sleep. Our diversions dwindle. When we touch one another, it is with the chill of death. In the darkness, by our feet, small things brush by us, sometimes lick us, feeling certain of their future. Forty days ago one of us screamed, and then cried. Since then, we have all been dry. Our lovemaking has been sporadic and desperate. We have lost joy in our worry. We have begged, we have offered our service, but we cannot leave. We get little response. Hope dies. Feel, listen to our hearts beating, beating, less and less. Our blood lies still. Our lungs are paralyzed, our limbs atrophied. Disease takes us away. Quietly, in corners, we slaughter one another, then kiss and make up, and then die. Do you hear me out there? Do you hear me? Do you hear me? This is Bubi, Bubi, of Bubi's Hide-Away. Answer, respond, acknowledge, communicate, relieve us, for we cannot last, we . . . cannot . . . *last.*

There is a long moment of silence. It is broken by EDWINA, *whom* EDWIN *drags forward.*

EDWINA Put me down, you stupid fuck child molester! I'll boil you in dirty oil! I'll put tetanus in your orange juice! I'll fill up your socks with wet prostitute snot! —Ahhh, Bubi, save me from this monstrous monster!

EDWIN Bubi, Edwina would like to try to get through.

BUBI You go right ahead, pumpkin.

EDWINA You call me a pumpkin again and I'll drill you full of holes. —I don't like that image. I withdraw it.

BUBI Of course, darling.

EDWINA *(Staring at* BUBI*)* Right! Gimme that mike. How come they never call these things Michelle, only Mike? Women are always getting screwed. —I don't like that image either. Knock on wood —Hey! *(Slapping* EDWIN*)* Cut that out! Holy Christ! I take them *all* back. You're trying to exterminate me, fartface, don't you try to lie your way out of it.

EDWIN Edwina, I love you.

EDWINA *(Holding her sore crotch)* Yeah, you proved that, all right. I should have stayed with the woodpecker. At least he was a gentleman.

BUBI Darling, you're monopolizing the mike.

EDWINA *(Smiling roguishly and cradling the microphone in her crotch)* Yeah. I always wanted a mike of my own. *(To* BUBI*)* I must have been out of my mind when I fell for you, baby. What are you smiling about? Take it from me, any guy that screws a two-year-old wooden dummy got plenty of problems of his own. *(Speaking into the microphone)* Hello, hello, I want to be connected with Moishe's pushcart on Orchard Street. *(To* BUBI*)* He'll know what to do. He'll get us out of this fix. *(Into the microphone)* What? You never heard of him? *(To* BUBI*)* How do you like that? They never heard of Moishe! *Can you believe it? Moishe. On Orchard Street. (Into the microphone)* What if I say Orchard *Strit?* —You're all dumb fucks. I spit on you all. I give you the back and front of my hand. May you all drop dead twice.

EDWIN *grabs the microphone from her, hands it quickly to* BUBI, *clamps his hand over* EDWINA*'s mouth, and drags her away.*

Moishe! . . . all dumb— Stop— Let me. . . . *(Quite clearly)* Get your thumb out of my ass!

EDWIN *finally subdues her. A long moment of silence.* BUBI *is anxiously looking at the* AUDIENCE*—what is left of it.*

BUBI Well, darlings? No cheers? No applause? No "Bubi!" You're all played out? There aren't too many of you left. *(Looking out over the theater as well as at the stage* AUDIENCE*)* Are there any more performers among you? Come on, now, don't be timid. This is no time to be timid. *(Whispering)* Come on, we *need* you.

All but two of the AUDIENCE *stand up. It is a motley group: bums, a fat lady, etc.* THEY *move in a slow, grotesque tableau toward* BUBI, *in time to the lyric* "Heute, heute, wirst du mit mir" *from Bach's Cantata No. 106, "Actus Tragicus." This music fades into the Lone Ranger theme, during which* THEY *mount one another and gallop or pump furiously. This fades into a conga, with suitable action, which in turn gives way to Cossack dance music. At the end, there is a mad potpourri of music and action until* THEY *fall down exhausted and unable to cope.*

EDWINA Moishe could do it better!

Laughter.

BUBI *(In French) Silence!*

THEY *all stare at the* AUDIENCE *until* BUBI *speaks.*

(To the lone remaining couple) Well, darlings, aren't you joining us?

YOUNG MAN *(After a pause)* The menu says there's no cover charge.

BUBI There's always a cover charge, darling, didn't you know?

YOUNG MAN *(Stubbornly)* The menu says there's no cover charge. We—we're on our honeymoon.

EDWINA Moishe could do it better!

Brief laughter.

BUBI *(Benignly, coaxing) Darlings.* Don't be foolish. You've just grown up. You're in love. Do you feel nothing? *Nothing?* Listen.

Jackhammers above.

Listen. *(He recites, in German, Rilke's "Der Panther"*)*

Sein Blick ist vom Vorübergehn der Stäbe
so müd geworden, dass er nichts mehr hält.
Ihm ist, als ob es tausend Stäbe gäbe
und hinter tausend Stäben keine Welt.

Der weiche Gang geschmeidig starker Schritte,
der sich im allekleinsten Kreise dreht,
ist wie ein Tanz von Kraft um eine Mitte,
in der betäubt ein grosser Wille steht.

Nur manchmal schiebt der Vorhang der Pupille
sich lautlos auf—. Dann geht ein Bild hinein,
geht durch der Glieder angespannte Stille—
und hört im Herzen auf zu sein.

A long moment of silence.

It is about a panther, a beautiful, sleek, black panther, in a cage, looking out, dumbly. And then, for one brief moment,

*A translation will be found on page 54.

the eye's film recedes, and the panther looks, and sees. *Sees,* Helen.

YOUNG WOMAN You . . . you know my name. . . . What does the panther see?

BUBI Ah, yes. What does the panther see? Don't you know? Have you never looked out? Come. *(Softly, seductively) Kommst. Venga, hija. Viens.*

Silence. The YOUNG WOMAN *rises, closes her eyes and feels herself gently.*

YOUNG MAN Helen. Helen! Sit down!

The YOUNG WOMAN *slowly takes off her clothes.*

Helen! What are you doing! Stop it!

When SHE *is naked,* SHE *walks slowly to the performers on* BUBI*'s stage and disappears within their communal embrace.*

(Screaming) Helen!

BUBI Come on, darling. You, too. Can you sing? Can you dance? Can you gargle?

YOUNG MAN The menu says there is no cover charge!

BUBI Darling, the lights are going.

Slow fade.

YOUNG MAN The menu says there is no cover charge! The menu says there is no cover charge!

Whistles outside. Loud bulldozer sounds. Crashing wood. The BARON, *now with a sword, enters, followed by the* VICE SQUAD.

THEY wear badges and dark glasses. HE barks incomprehensible commands at them. THEY march, line up at attention, etc., strip down to panties, garter belts, long black stockings, and brassieres, then stand at attention again. At the BARON's command THEY drag the YOUNG MAN to a makeshift guillotine and behead him as HE is screaming, "No! . . . No! . . . The menu says there is no cover charge! . . ." A spot on BUBI as HE picks up the head and places it on a table. HE then speaks out to the theater audience.

BUBI *(With profound love and sincerity)* Well, darlings, do you know now how very much I love you? I'm so pleased you've come to Bubi's Hide-Away. We need you, we want you. Some of you, I know, have come from far away. Some of you have doubts, fears. You've come for many reasons. But you've *come.* And you are all welcome, you are all my darlings. I do love you so. I know you have things to show me. Tricks, songs, dances. I know I shall love them all. And you mustn't worry. You don't have to be a sensation for me. Give me whatever you've got. Roll your eyes, smack your lips, wiggle your fingers even. When I call you, when it's your turn, just come up and let us see what you have. *Please,* you must not be afraid. *(Imitating the BARON) Bubi lufs everybody! (HE laughs gently. The spot begins to fade)* We have a long way to go, such a long way, all of us, and we're all so tired, so tired and lonely. Darlings, come to Bubi. Come to Bubi. Let Bubi hold you. Let Bubi love you. Let Bubi keep you safe. Come. Come to Bubi. . . .

HE sings. As he sings, the spot fades completely on him, and a pin light comes up on the YOUNG MAN's head.

Come to Bubi's Hide-Away.
You know what people say.
You'll get more for what you pay
At Bubi's Hide-Away.

Come to Bubi's Hide-Away.
Come to Bubi's, come to play.

Come to Bubi's, night or day,
To Bubi's Hide-Away.

Come to Bubi's Hide-Away.
You can curse or you can pray.
You can lie or you can lay
At Bubi's Hide-Away.

Come to Bubi's, we shall sleep.
Come to Bubi's, we shall keep
All your troubles far away
At Bubi's Hide-Away.

Slowly, the eyes in the YOUNG MAN*'s head open, the head moves and turns almost upright. With great difficulty, the mouth moves, then speaks.*

YOUNG MAN *(At first in whispers, then finally a hoarse croak)* Bubi! Bubi! Bubi! Bubi! Bubi! Bubi! Bubi! Bubi! . . .

HE *is drowned out by the sound of bulldozers and jackhammers advancing into the theater. The light fades quickly. The bulldozer and jackhammer sounds give way to the sound of many wings, as of ducks and geese flying high in the sky.*

Notes: Translations of the poems recited by BUBI.

Jean Racine, *Phèdre*, III, 2, 813–822

O Venus, relentless witness to my abject shame,
Have I not suffered enough?
Your cruel designs have all succeeded:
I am love's slave.
Test now your barbs on someone more resistant:
Hippolytus, whom your very name seems to offend,
Scorns to worship at your altar.
O God of Love, avenge me! Our goals are one!

Rainer Maria Rilke, "Der Panther"

His sight from ever gazing through the bars
has grown so blunt that it sees nothing more.
It seems to him that thousands of bars are
before him, and behind them nothing merely.

The easy motion of his supple stride,
which turns about the very smallest circle,
is like a dance of strength about a center
in which a mighty will stands stupefied.

Only sometimes when the pupil's film
soundlessly opens . . . then one image fills
and glides through the quiet tension of the limbs
into the heart and ceases and is still.

The Moke-Eater: Jack (center)
meets the citizens of Monte Waite

THE MOKE-EATER

The Moke-Eater was first performed by the Play-House of the Ridiculous at Max's Kansas City restaurant in New York on September 19, 1968. It was directed by John Vaccaro, with set and costume designs by the company, music by Jesse T. West, taped sounds by Tony Conrad, film sequences by Bill Gamble, and the following cast:

American Eagle *Harpies Bizarre*
Men *Aubrey Hardon, Henrietta Big Pink, Marie Antoinette, Kalila Gaboon, Jesse T. West, Baby Bettie Moses*
Mechanic *Claude Purvis*
Jack *Bruce Pecheur*
Clowns *Patsy LaMars, David Grunion-Gaboon*
Alec *Sierra Bandit*
Maria *Elsene Sorrentino*
Old Man *One of the Gaboons*
Crow *Rene Ricard*
Musicians *Jesse T. West, Adrian Cathcart*
Acrobats *The Three Gaboons: Kalila, Kalil, and David*
Waiter *One of the Gaboons*
Color Guard *Jesse T. West, Adrian Cathcart, One of the Gaboons*
Harrington *Rene Ricard*
Sybil *Patsy LaMars*
The Moke-Eater *By Herself*

This production subsequently played at the Cafe Au Go-Go, and was revived in the spring of 1969 for a third set of performances at the Gotham Art Theatre.

As the theater lights dim, but before the curtain rises, there is a minute of primitive drum beats, low but persistent. As they fade away, the curtain rises on the town square of Monte Waite, a gray, shabby, backwater New England community. Most of the stage is taken up with a ramshackle, unpainted boarding house, the first floor of which is a restaurant-bar. There are few walls to speak of; the scene becomes whatever the action requires. Inside there are several doors, a bar, tables and chairs. All this is in shadow until the action moves into the bar. Outside there is a porch with broken wicker chairs on which some OLD MEN *sit motionless. Periodically the shutters of the windows on the second floor open, then shut, but no one is ever seen.* PEOPLE *stand and sit listlessly in the street, across which a faded, torn, unreadable banner hangs loosely. No one seems conscious of anyone else. No one talks. There are no women. A heavily uniformed and goggled* STATE TROOPER *rides through slowly on a motor bike.* HE *looks at nothing. No one pays any attention to him. Now and then, someone starts, looks up or into the distance, as if he has heard something. The sound of a far-off car is heard. As the sound becomes more distinct, it is apparent that the car has motor trouble. Somehow this gains the attention of everyone. There is a low murmur as* THEY *look off stage. The* OLD MEN *on the porch lean forward. The car coughs to a stop, still out of sight. There is utter silence. No one moves. Then a car door slams and a tenor voice calls out.*

JACK *(Off)* Hey. Anybody here? *(*HE *whistles)* Hello? Hello? . . . Hey. *(*HE *kicks his fender)* Hey! Hey! Paisano!

HE *toots his horn nervously. There is a tremor of excitement among the* MEN. THEY *strain forward eagerly, though* THEY *do not move.*

Hey! Hellooo! Gas man! Chop-chop! Business! *(*HE *waits)* What the hell? What kind of one-horse town . . . *Hey! (*HE *appears suddenly on stage and stops short, seeing all the men.* HE *is of medium height, somewhat overweight, clean-shaven, and both aggressive and timid looking by turns.* HE *wears a sporty fedora* *with feathers in it)* Well, bless my cotton-picking soul. *(*HE *takes off his hat, smooths his hair, then puts on the hat again)* It ain't a ghost town after all. Whataya know. Hiya, fellers. Say, where's a mechanic in this community? *(No answer)* I'm in a hurry. Where . . . Isn't there anyone on duty at . . . the . . . *(*HE *is becoming slightly apprehensive because of the silent, intense attention focused on him)* Say, is there an attendant here? Who's in charge of you? I mean . . .

The MEN *begin mumbling.*

*(*JACK *laughs nervously)* Noisy cusses, aren't you? . . .

THEY *quiet down.*

Which . . . of you runs the gas station? . . . *(*HE *shrugs, looks at the audience)*

There is some hesitation among the MEN. *They bunch up, knocking into one another clumsily, mumbling incoherently as they do throughout the play. Finally* THEY *nudge one of their number forward, a gangling* MAN *in overalls who appears to be a mechanic.* JACK *eyes him sarcastically.*

Atta boy. Now isn't that more like it? Huh? Sure it is. Listen, fellers, I don't bite. Honest.

THEY *are silent a minute. Then, to his surprise as well as theirs,* JACK *barks and the* MAN *jumps.*

Ha ha ha!

MECHANIC *(Wide-eyed, shuffling up to* JACK *spasmodically, with a rural twang)* H-h-h-hello, Fred. *(*HE *jerks* JACK*'s hand nervously)*

JACK *(After a pause)* Come again? Fred? Uh-uh. Jack's the name.

MECHANIC M-m-m-mighty glad to see you, Fred. We been waitin'. *(HE laughs stupidly to himself)*

JACK *(Laughing briefly)* Hell's bells. I'm not your Fred, buddy. What is this, a joke? Huh? Huh?

MECHANIC That's all right, Fred. We-we-we-we understand. *(HE grins weirdly at JACK)*

JACK *(Scratching his head and looking around)* You do, huh? Well, I don't know about that now, I don't know. *(Silence)* Say, I don't know what's going on around here, but . . . *(HE points to the banner overhead)* What have you got, a festival or something going on? . . . A summer festival? Huh? *(Talking now to the other MEN, becoming involved in a situation without realizing it)* Hey. What's wrong with number-one boy here, huh? *(Nodding his head like a horse)* That's right, I said what's wrong with number-one boy here? Not too bright? . . . Huh? *(HE puts his arms around the MECHANIC)* You fixee cars? You grease-monkey boy, chop-chop? *(HE laughs abruptly, stops when he feels the silence again)* Hey! What gives? Are you a bunch of loonies? Where's the guy that runs the gas station? *(A little angrily, asserting himself)* Come on, come on. I can take a joke as well as the next guy, but let's get this show on the road.

Clash of cymbals. A three-piece, gaily dressed CLOWN BAND *comes clattering out of the bar.*

FIRST CLOWN What falls out of the sky?

SECOND CLOWN Rain.

The three CLOWNS *laugh hilariously, suddenly stop.*

FIRST CLOWN What lies on the ground?

SECOND CLOWN Turd.

THIRD CLOWN What?

The CLOWNS *laugh again and suddenly stop.*

JACK *(Mock-pleading)* Aw, give me a break, fellers. *(Silence)* Huh? *(Dramatizing)* I swear I didn't do it, fellers. I never seen the old lady before in my life. Them other guys lied. She was dead when I got there. I swear I didn't do it!

The MEN *mumble excitedly.*

Hey. Hey, hold on now, take it easy, fellers. Slow down. Whoa. I was only *joking.*

The mumbling becomes threatening.

Hey, you guys are nuts. What are you doing? Stop! *(*HE *whips out his wallet, takes out bills)* Here. Look. Money. Fix my car, okay? That's all. Just fix my car. Come on, fellers. *Please!*

The mumbling subsides. JACK *looks at them a minute.*

Look. *(With pantomime)* Me Jack. Me got car.

HE *makes a sound like a motor. The* MEN *give a faint moronic laugh.*

Car no good. Car go click-click. Car bad. Me want fix car. Me pay. *(*HE *waves the money)* You understandee 'melican boy? Chop-chop?

MAN *(From the edge of the crowd)* Click-click?

JACK *(Relieved)* Yesss. *Very* good. Click-click. That's it exactly. You've got it down beautifully.

MEN *(In complete confusion)* Click, click, click, click-click . . .

JACK Yeah. That's it, fellers. Click-click. Car go click-click.

The MEN *continue repeating the click-click. Their excitement rises until it seems* THEY *are about to burst loose into some violent action.* JACK *backs away, is about to turn and run when* ALEC *comes through the crowd, holding his hand in the air.* HE *is thin, dapper, with his hair slicked back.* HE *wears a checkered vest, tight black pants, and shiny, pointed shoes.*

ALEC Stop!

The MEN *immediately subside.* HE *turns to* JACK.

Hello, there. I'm Alec. *(*HE *pauses) Smart* Alec. *(*HE *laughs loudly at his joke, then extends his hand to* JACK. *In a western drawl)* Welcome, stranger. We ain't hardly seen a coyote since the dry spell came. How's the water over yonder, pardner?

JACK The water? . . . *(Taking his hand gingerly)* Well . . . I'm glad to meet . . . Say, are *you* the—

ALEC *whips around suddenly, snaps his fingers vigorously several times at the* BAND, *and taps his foot in rhythm to get them started.* THEY *play a slow, heavy march with many mistakes, petering out at the end.* ALEC *looks at* JACK *proudly throughout.*

ALEC *(With great enthusiasm)* Welcome. Welcome! *Welcome! (*HE *kisses* JACK *generously on the cheeks. In a French accent)* Ah, monsieur, eet is a grate plaisir. *(Kissing the air)* Ummmmph!

The MEN *cheer moronically. The* BAND *attempts a feeble chord.*

JACK *(Faintly, in disbelief)* Huh?

ALEC *(Pounding him on the back in a voice like that of Bugs Bunny or some other Walt Disney cartoon character)* My boy, my boy!

MECHANIC *(Shuffling up and hugging* JACK *frantically)* Fwed! Fwed! *(Agonizingly)* Fwed! *(*HE *cries)*

MEN *(Rushing up to hug and touch him)* Fwed! Fwed! *(Some of them wipe tears away)* Fwed! *(*THEY *swarm over him)*

JACK *(Buried in the crowd)* Hey. Hey, come on, fellers. Ha ha. Cut it out. Ha ha ha. Hey! *(Desperately)* Hey! Hey! Stop! Help! Help me! Ahhhhhh!

ALEC, *swinging and snapping a whip, breaks through to him.* HE *pulls off the last few clinging hands roughly.* JACK *is in rags.*

ALEC Pay no attention to them. They're just overwrought. They're just so happy. *(Sincerely, clapping his hands)* Fred, they're *so happy.*

JACK *(Frantic)* Overwrought? Happy? Who-who-who- the hell cares? Look at my clothes. Eighty dollars! They're maniacs! Crazy maniacs! Let me out of here!

Everything is suddenly silent. The creaky sound of a guillotine blade being pulled up, then its smooth descent, then the thud of a head being sliced off.

ALEC *(Ominously)* Fred, they are very sensitive. Please. Remember what they have already endured for you.

JACK Huh? What? What was that noise?

Silence. The sound of the guillotine again, this time followed by the heavy grunt of onlookers.

ALEC *(Soothingly)* Fred, it's spring again. Isn't that wonderful? And Fred. They are very tired from waiting. Very tired. It has all been . . . so very . . . tiring . . . Fred. Do you understand?

JACK Tired? *(Mocking)* Oh, ho, ho, ho. Yeah, yeah. Well, what about my clothes, huh? What about that? You think I can go anywhere like this?

ALEC *(Bowing, in a Chinese accent)* Velly solly. Chinee boy velly solly. Shall give honorable gent new clothes. *(*HE *mutters some nasal Chinese sounds, then resumes his normal voice)* After, of course, we have taken measurements.

JACK *(A little dazed)* Naturally. . . . Well, I should hope so. *(*HE *tries to brush himself off and repair some of the damage)*

ALEC *(Conspiratorially)* Psst! Psst! Fred!

JACK Damn it all, I'm not—

ALEC Shhh!

JACK *(Softly)* Fred.

MEN Fwed! Fwed!

THEY *begin mumbling and crowding forward in their peculiar, always ominous shuffle, but* ALEC *turns and quiets them by holding up his hands.*

ALEC *(Out of the side of his mouth)* Look happy, you damn fool. They've been waiting for you.

JACK *gives the* MEN *a strained smile.*

MEN Fwed! Fwed! Fwed!

JACK *(Whispering)* What do you mean they've been waiting for me?

ALEC *(Slipping him a beer-can opener)* Here. Take it.

JACK Huh? What the hell? What's it for?

ALEC Shhh! It's all I can give you. You may have to dig your way out. Listen carefully. There is great *(Spelling)* D-A-N-G-E-R here. We are in a time of *(Spelling)* C-R-I-S-I-S. If you don't have faith in me *(Suddenly changing his tone)* you will die, white man. *(HE laughs like a stage villain)*

JACK Wha—?

ALEC *(Turning to the crowd and clearing his throat)* Friends, neighbors, citizens of Monte Waite, I know I speak for all of you when I say to our honored, our long-awaited, guest, welcome, *Welcome,* Fred, to Monte Waite.

HE *turns, beaming, to* JACK *as the crowd screams like a collection of lunatics. A pretty* GIRL *in peasant costume runs out and puts a garland around* JACK*'s neck, giggles, and runs back.* ALEC *holds up his hand. There is silence.*

Men of Monte Waite, it is a day we have long awaited. We are a community hoary with history.

Cheers.

We have given just share to the cause

Cheers.

And it is only fitting, only right, that in our midst, in our time of travail, should come . . .

HE *turns to* JACK. *The cheering rises.* ALEC *holds up his hand again. Silence.*

Men of Monte Waite, I give you Fred!

The cheering explodes again. The MEN *rush to* JACK *in a body and carry him to the porch, ripping off half his rags in the pro-*

cess. Then they back off slightly. JACK *is bewildered and frightened.*

JACK *(Just a noise)* Uhhhhhhhhhh.

ALEC *(From behind the crowd, harshly)* Speak, you damn fool. Tell them what they've been waiting to hear.

JACK Wha-wha-wha—? *(*HE *looks around desperately)*

ALEC Make a speech!

JACK About what?

ALEC *(Harshly)* Speak!

MEN *(Mumbling incoherently)* Fwed! Fwed! Fwed!

JACK *holds up his hands weakly.* THEY *are silent.*

JACK Well, fellers *(Giggling nervously),* I—I sure am glad to be here.

HE *looks around apprehensively, totally unable to fathom his situation. The* MEN *listen with open, drooling mouths and expectant looks.*

I have heard of the, ah, the splendid fishing here and *(Noticing the* MEN *looking at one another questioningly)* the . . . ah, hunting and the, ah, lakes and woods, ah . . . yes. The woods. *(*HE *pauses, sees that the* MEN *are still looking at one another)* And of course I have known of Monte Waite's great . . . great historical role in, ah, history. Yes.

His last words are drowned out in garbled cheering. He feels he is on the right track and shows more confidence.

Monte Waite's name will live forever in the hearts of men and in the annals of, ah, history.

Cheers.

It is a deep and sincere . . . honor to, ah, be here.

Cheers.

Monte Waite is, ah, a bulwark of . . . ah, our way of life.

Cheers.

The American way of life.

Cheers, then deathlike silence. JACK *is taken aback and is momentarily unable to speak.*

That's why I want to say to you . . .

MEN *(Agonizingly)* Fwed! Fwed! Fwed!

JACK . . . to say to you that, that . . . that the time has come!

Wild cheering.

And I hope that in my humble way that, that . . . that I can contribute to, to, ah . . . *what is to come!*

Wild cheering.

And . . . and . . . well, now about me, I guess . . . Well, my name is Jack, and—

The mumbling becomes threatening.

My name is Fred!

Cheers.

Fred! Yes, ah, Fred.

More cheers, scattered moans of "Fwed!"

And I'm, well, I'm just a salesman. And I'm awfully glad to be here. As I'm sure you all, ah, know, Monte Waite is distinctly in my territory. You might say it's right at the center. Ha ha.

The mumbling begins again, slowly rising as HE *speaks so that* HE *has to keep raising his voice, finally shouting.*

I, ah, carry a complete line of paper. From, ah, legal paper to toilet paper. The whole works. Ha ha. If it's on paper, we've got it! I say if it's on paper, we've got it. We have nothing but the best! The *Best! (The noise begins to frighten him again)* I have a wife and two children! A boy and a girl! One more in the oven! *(Almost screaming)* I said I have one more in the oven! And I have a dog! *(Desperately)* Long live Monte Waite!

Suddenly, complete silence. Sound of guillotine again, followed by collective groan. JACK *wipes his face and head with a handkerchief.*

Well. Well, gee whiz. And then there's the situation with my car. A Dodge. Not the latest model, of course.

ALEC Louder, Fred.

JACK *(Excessively loud)* It's a *Dodge!* There was something wrong with the *motor!*

MAN *(After a pause)* Click-click?

JACK Ha ha. Yes, that's it. It was going . . . ah . . .

MAN Click-click?

The MEN *repeat the sound until a kind of pandemonium is reached.*

ALEC Stop! Stop!

Silence. Sound of guillotine again, followed by collective grunt.

Three cheers for Fred! Hip-hip—

MEN Fwed!

ALEC Hip-hip—

MEN Fwed!

ALEC Hip-hip—

MEN Fwed!

JACK *(Moving off the porch, nodding his head as if thanking them for the honor, and mumbling)* Mighty obliged for—

ALEC Not yet! Get back! You're not done!

JACK *freezes in his tracks.*

I said get back! Get back!

JACK *(Stepping back)* But, but . . . *(Pathetically)* I wanna go. I don't wanna stay anymore. Please mister, have a heart. I mean, for God's sake, a joke is a joke. I don't want to get you in any trouble. Live and let live. Listen, I mind my own business. I—I got a *territory* to cover.

ALEC *(Laughing sharply)* You can't go. You think you can get off so easily?

JACK *cries briefly like a baby.*

No, no. You've much more. These men have been waiting for you. These men have been *dying* for you to come. You can't escape. You've got to satisfy them. Now. This minute. This second. Can you sing?

JACK *(Pointing nervously)* Y-y-y-you're crazy, mister. I don't understand *any*thing you're talking about, and-and-and I think you're crazy.

MAN *(Moronically)* Cwazy, Fwed.

ALEC *(Imperiously) Can you sing,* you fathead?

MAN *(Moronically)* Cwazy, Fwed. *(*HE *laughs)*

JACK *(Stepping back in fear)* But, but . . .

ALEC *(Thundering) Answer!*

JACK Wha—? Well, yes, I guess so. I mean I've, I've sung. I mean not professionally or anything, but . . .

ALEC Good. Do you know the tune, "I'm sitting on top of the world?"

JACK Well, yes. I've heard it.

ALEX Sing it! *(As* JACK *hesitates)* Sing it! *(*HE *snaps the whip)*

JACK *(In a wobbly voice, accompanied badly by the three-piece* BAND*)* I'm sitting on top of the world . . .

ALEC Tap dance!

JACK Wha-what?

ALEC Tap dance! *(As* JACK *tries to tap dance)* While you sing, you fool!

JACK *(Completely intimidated)* Oh. Sorry. *(Singing and dancing)* I'm sitting on top of the world . . .

ALEC Wave your arms! Smile!

JACK *(Singing, tap dancing, waving his arms, and smiling a smile of sheer terror)* I'm sitting on top of the world/Just a-rolling along /Just a-singing a song . . .

When HE *is done the* MEN *cry out "Fwed! Fwed," some of them sobbing as if he has satisfied a great need.* JACK *tries cautiously to get down.*

ALEC *(Snapping his whip)* Back! Get back!

JACK *jumps back.*

That was splendid, Fred. You had the true spirit of music in you.

JACK Thank you. *(*HE *half bows, half curtsies)*

ALEC Now, by your feet, that paper.

JACK *looks down.*

Pick it up.

JACK *does.*

Now read it.

JACK *(Reading with a little difficulty)* "Amos: Who was that woman I saw you—"

ALEC *(Screaming)* No, no, no! You don't have the accent. Don't you know the southern dialect? Don't you know how to imitate the southern dialect? *(*HE *claps his hands)* Maria!

The same pretty GIRL *comes out, this time dressed as a southern belle, rubs shoe polish on* JACK*'s cheeks and forehead, puts a wig of negro hair on his head, hands him a tambourine, giggles and runs back.*

Better. Much better. You make a lovely Negro. Now do it again. And remember. The southern dialect.

JACK *(Reading with a southern dialect)* "Amos: Who was dat woman I saw you wid last night, Kingfish? Kingfish: Dat wasn't no woman, Amos. Dat was mah wife." *(*HE *looks up in stunned silence, his eyes very white)*

ALEC Laugh.

JACK *(Weakly)* What?

ALEC Laugh!

JACK Ha ha ha.

ALEC Wave the tambourine.

JACK *(Waving the tambourine)* Ha ha ha.

ALEC No, no, no! The southern dialect, man!

JACK *(In southern dialect)* Ho, ho, ho. *(*HE *shakes the tambourine)*

ALEC More!

JACK Ho, ho, ho, ho, hawr! Ho, ho, ho, ho, hawr!

ALEC More!

JACK *(Forcing belly laughs and shaking the tambourine wildly)* Oh, ho, ho, ho, ho, hawr! Haw, haw, haw, ho, ho, ho, ho, hawr, whee!

The MEN *grin big wide grins at one another, but nothing comes out of their oral cavities except moronic moans.*

ALEC Now do it again.

JACK Again?

ALEC Yes. We want it to be . . . perfect.

JACK The same way?

ALEC Exactly.

JACK *(Reading with southern dialect)* "Amos: Who was dat woman I saw you wid last night, Kingfish? Kingfish: Dat wasn't no woman, Amos. Dat was mah wife." *(*HE *laughs as before, then stops abruptly and looks at* ALEC *with a deadpan look)*

ALEC Very good, Fred. Very good indeed. Ha ha ha. Very good. I knew you had a few up your sleeve. Now turn it over. *(*JACK *turns the paper over)* Someone get him a box. Maria!

The pretty GIRL *comes out again, this time in pioneer costume, puts a box under him, giggles, and runs back.*

Get on it. Quick.

JACK *steps up on the box.* HE *looks extremely uncomfortable.*

Look sad. Make believe you are Abraham Lincoln pondering the great issues of his time.

JACK *looks serious.*

Now, as you read, cry. Cry as if you mean it. I want your heart to break. Do you understand? Break!

JACK *stares at him with glazed eyes.*

Damn you, man, I asked you a question!

JACK Wha-wha-what if I can't cry. I mean—

ALEC *(In a western drawl)* You'd better, pardner, if'n you don't want to leave here feet first. *(*HE *laughs like Walt Disney's Bugs Bunny. In his regular voice)* Now read!

JACK *(Reading, not very sadly, and unsuccessful in his efforts to cry)*

To one who bears the sweetest name,
And adds a lustre—

ALEC Damn you, fool! Idiot! Imbecile! Do you want to be drawn and quartered? I said as if your heart were breaking! Maria!

The pretty GIRL, *dressed severely as a Puritan, runs out with a huge curved Oriental knife, holds it to* JACK*'s throat, and giggles. The* STATE TROOPER *rides through slowly.*

All right, that's enough.

HE *claps his hands, and* SHE *runs back.*

Does that help, Fred?

JACK *(Genuinely crying from fear)*

To one who bears the sweetest name,
And adds a lustre to the same,
Who shares my joy
And cheers when sad,

The greatest friend I ever had,
Long life to her, for there's none other
Can take the place of my dear mother.

JACK *breaks down completely and the crowd cheers madly.*

ALEC Splendid. Splendid. A touch of the poet.

JACK Now can I go? Huh? *(*HE *sees the* MECHANIC *and calls to him weakly)* Hey. Hey, you. Where's my car? Is it fixed? *(*HE *fumbles for his wallet, takes out all his money and throws it limply in front of him)* Here. Take it all.

The MECHANIC *looks into the distance. There is a loud, grinding crash.* HE *turns to* JACK *with a smile, shrugs, and slowly shakes his head.*

My, my car? *(Sinking down)* Ohhhh. My car! My *car!* What did you do to it? How can I leave?

ALEC White man never leave. *(*HE *laughs like a cartoon character. In his normal voice)* A trifle, Fred, a mere trifle. *(*HE *walks forward and lifts* JACK *up)* Accept our hospitality for the night, Fred. There's none better than the Monte Waite Inn. *(*HE *snaps his whip at the men)* Get in there, you! Get in!

The MEN *mumble and fall over one another in their scramble up the steps. A few linger at the door, waiting.* ALEC *speaks to* JACK *confidentially.*

You did beautifully, Fred. They've taken you to their hearts. Don't let them down. *(*HE *puts his arm around* JACK*'s shoulder)* I hope you didn't take me seriously back there. I had to do all that. Part of the show. They're very sensitive. Surely you see that now. Listen, the last man we had drawn and quartered, well . . . *(*HE *giggles)* Shall we say he was a fool? *(*HE *giggles again)* We strung him up till he turned a rainbow purple, then cut him down and threw water on him. The fellow didn't know where he was. *(*HE *giggles)* He thought it was all over. But it wasn't. Oh, not by a long shot. *(*HE *giggles)* When he finally knew where he was again, then we cut off his . . . privates. Slowly. You should have seen his face. *(*HE *giggles)* When we chopped off his arms and legs, he couldn't believe it. He couldn't take it all in. He almost looked indignant. He was really speechless. *(*HE *giggles)* And then he thought we were just going to let him die. He almost looked happy, you know the feeling, the worst is over? That was when we stuck the knife in his abdomen and began turning it around.

JACK *looks at him horrified.* ALEC *nods his head and laughs eagerly.*

Yes. Yes. The same knife! He wasn't so speechless then, I'll tell you. He spoke plenty. But you know we couldn't understand a word! *(*HE *explodes into laughter)* We threw his intestines all over him. We cut out his liver and stuffed it into his mouth, as much of it as we could. And, and, wait, will you believe it? *(*HE *can hardly contain himself)* I think we actually choked him with it! *(*HE *laughs without control)* The fool choked on his own liver! *(*HE *bends over laughing, finally breaking into a coughing fit, then coming to himself)* Oh, it's a great life, I tell you, Fred, if you don't weaken. You didn't think for a minute I meant anything, did you, Fred? Oh, really, now. *(Earnestly)* It's all part of the show! *(*HE *pats him on the back)* Come on now. Let's have some fun. I think I can promise you a very good time. These fellows, they're *very* sensitive. They *adore* you, simply *adore* you. You wouldn't mind a little fun, would you? *(*HE *pokes him playfully)* Eh? Eh? Come on, Fred, relax. Laugh a little.

JACK Ha ha.

ALEC That's it. Again.

JACK Ha ha. Ha ha ha.

ALEC Good fellow. And listen. Inside, relax. Let them see that you're having the time of your life. Eh? Eh?

JACK Ha ha. Ha ha ha.

ALEC Splendid.

During this exchange, an OLD MAN *has been slowly hobbling down the street with a cane. The* MEN *at the door begin mumbling the instant they see him, their excitement mounting as* HE *comes closer. When* HE *is in front of the bar* THEY *begin hurling indistinct imprecations at him. The* OTHERS *come out and join them until their fury overflows and* THEY *swoop down on him, fists and sticks flying.*

JACK *(Touching* ALEC*)* Hey. Hey, look what they're doing. They're, they're . . . They'll kill him.

ALEC Precisely. You're too sensitive, my boy. It's all good clean fun. Pay no attention.

The MEN *retreat as suddenly as they attacked.* THEY *cower by the porch, mumbling, watching the crumpled heap that was the* OLD MAN. *After a few minutes,* THEY *push* ONE *of their number out.* HE *advances and retreats, gradually approaching the* OLD MAN. HE *very warily puts out a finger and touches him, at which the* OLD MAN *groans. The* MAN *squeals in fright and shuffles back to the others. Slowly the* OLD MAN *begins to move. With great difficulty* HE *drags himself down the street and out of sight.*

JACK Who w-w-was . . .

ALEC A swine. The leader of the opposition party.

JACK W-w-what party is that?

ALEC The birthday party. *(*HE *laughs heartily at his joke)* Yuk, yuk, yuk! *(Seriously)* He's always agitating. You saw him. When he gets a taste of his own medicine he whines like a sick dog. I have no sympathy with such double dealing. The man is an outright swine. *(Snapping his whip at the* MEN*)* In! I say in! Get in!

The MEN *stumble into the bar and crowd into a corner, mumbling.*

Splendid fellows, don't you think? Well now, Fred, some refreshment? Yes? Oh, here, my boy. *(*HE *hands* JACK *a dinner tie)* Put it on, go on, it's all right. *(*HE *helps* JACK *tie it)* There now. You could go anywhere. Would you like gloves?

JACK Er, no, thank you.

ALEC Splendid. Now we may enter. After you. *(Whispering)* Remember! Look happy!

HE *bows* JACK *in, as the lights brighten.* THEY *sit at a table.* JACK *stares at* TWO MEN *and a* WOMAN *perched on a trapeze.*

Do you like them, Fred? Pet crows. *Very* intelligent. I've trained them to poke eyes out. How are you, my pets?

CROWS Guark! Guark! Guark!

ALEC Hungry, little darlings?

CROWS Guark! Guark! Guark! Guark!

ALEC Precious, aren't they? *(*HE *pecks a kiss at them)* Do you want Daddy to sing to you? Hmm?

CROWS Guark! Guark! Guark! *(*THEY *flap their arms)*

ALEC *gets up, briefly tunes a mandolin, and sings sweetly:*

ALEC There were three ravens
Sat on a tree,
Down, a-down . . .

At the end of his song, HE *takes some bits of food from the bar and feeds the* BIRDS, *who now crow contentedly at him, and returns to the table.*

Well now, the food, eh? Let's wine and dine. *(Clapping his hands)* Maria.

The pretty GIRL, *her hair done up and now dressed in a long, low-cut, svelte, black gown, brings out champagne and glasses.*

I think we'll have the French menus this time, my dear.

SHE *pulls up her dress, reaches under, brings out two menus, giggles, and leaves.*

Good. Good. *(Scrutinizing the menu)* Let's see now. Are you reading the menu?

JACK Huh? Yes. But I'm afraid I don't read French.

ALEC Jackass. It's in English. These are Chinese translations in the parentheses. But if you take the first letter of each word you can read it in phonetic Swahili.

JACK *(Looking at the menu closely. It is obviously in French)* Oh.

ALEC Do you know Swahili?

JACK No.

ALEC Nor I. Stupid, isn't it? I recommend the chicken head.

JACK Well, I always liked—

ALEC Yes? *(Menacingly)* Do tell me what you liked, Freddie.

JACK Well, I like chicken pretty well.

ALEC Splendid. With the natural juices?

JACK Oh. Yes.

ALEC Splendid. Shall we have steamed skunk cabbage with it?

JACK Oh, sure. Whatever you think.

ALEC *(Slamming his hand on the table angrily)* It isn't what I think that matters! It's what *you* think! For God's sake, man, be independent! Think for yourself!

JACK Well, no, I was always partial to . . . steamed—

ALEC Splendid. *(*HE *grabs* JACK*'s menu and puts it away with his. Then* HE *opens the champagne)* Wait. Lights!

Brilliant lighting.

Music! *(Six Viennese musicians, formally dressed but with real monkey tails, come out and play waltz music.* ALEC *pours two glasses of champagne)*

Now, a toast.

JACK *(Holding up his glass)* A toast.

ALEC *(Angrily)* To what?

JACK Oh. To, ah, health. To health all right?

ALEC *(Solemnly)* To health. *(Just before* HE *drinks, but as* JACK *is already drinking, in a low voice)* Mine.

MARIA *slinks out and stands by* JACK.

MARIA *(Seductively, in a Hungarian accent)* You vant pretzel, baby?

JACK *hesitates.*

ALEC Take it.

JACK Well . . . all right.

MARIA, *smiling seductively at* JACK, *slowly takes a pretzel from between her breasts and holds it in front of his nose.*

ALEC Take it, you fool. Eat it.

JACK *eats the pretzel rapidly.*

MARIA You vant anodder pretzel, baby, huh?

JACK *(After a slight hesitation)* All—all right.

MARIA *(Leaning her bosom into his face)* So take, darlink.

ALEC What the hell are you waiting for?

JACK *pokes his finger between* MARIA*'s breasts.* SHE *squirms and giggles.* JACK *turns red with awkward delight. Her squirming makes finding the pretzel more difficult. Finally* HE *comes up with it, and* MARIA *sweeps away laughing in a low voice.*

JACK *(To* ALEC*)* Ha ha. Funny. Good trick. Ha ha.

ALEC *(With contempt)* Why don't you keep those skinny lips of yours closed tight! *(Suddenly changing his mood)* Now, my boy, some entertainment— Wait. You. Musicians. Take a break.

The MUSICIANS *put down their instruments and walk to the bar. The music, which has all along come from a phonograph behind them, continues.*

All right, all right! That's enough.

THEY *return. One of them resets the needle, and they take up their instruments and play.* ALEC *winks at* JACK. *In a cowboy drawl:*

Treat 'em rough, hey, pardner? Har, har, har.

JACK *nods faintly.*

*(*ALEC *claps his hands)* First act! First act!

THREE ACROBATS, *two men and a woman, come out and go through a clumsy routine of balancing tricks, taking bows after each trick. The waltz music continues.*

You see those two, Fred?

JACK Which?

ALEC Isn't it obvious which I mean?

JACK Oh. Ha ha. Yes. Excuse me.

ALEC They are husband and wife. The other one, he is the brother of the girl. The man is his sister. Clever, don't you think? He is also an uncle. The boy is also the father of the girl and the father of one of her twins. Siamese. She is his cousin. He is divorced from her niece and is now her lover. The other is the children's godfather and also the girl's half-brother by a former marriage. They were betrothed in the cradle, though he is old enough to be her son. She is only twenty-one today, and still a virgin. Have you ever seen a more beautiful creature? Forty-six strains of blood run through her veins, including Mongolian, Aztec, Irish, Cretan, Eskimo, Royal Canadian, French Canadian, Lithuanian, and Israeli. Her mother was a converted Arab born of a camel during a time of great drought. I believe there is also horse blood somewhere in her ancestry. Don't you adore her?

JACK Yes. She is . . . ah, very, very beautiful.

ALEC *(Coaxing)* Enter into it, man.

JACK *(Trying to be gay)* She's really very . . . pretty.

ALEC *(Avuncularly)* My boy, my boy. Uh, uh, uh. You shall have her if you wish. Nothing, *nothing*, is too good for the son of the crown prince.

JACK Thank you. Thank you very much.

ALEC *(Snorting)* 'S'nothing. 'S'nothing at all. Beautiful creature. Shaves her entire body every day. Fascinating thing to watch. Positively indecent. Uh-uh-uh! Beautiful, isn't she?

JACK Yes.

ALEC *(In his normal voice, angrily)* Not her, you fool! The other one!

JACK Oh.

ALEC Well?

JACK I—

ALEC Better. Much better. *(*HE *laughs and claps his hands)* All right! All right! Next! Gypsy dancers!

The ACROBATS *leave. The* MUSICIANS *put on false moustaches, open up their shirts, and don bandannas. The waltz music scratches to a halt.* MARIA *comes out in gypsy costume, her hair flowing.* SHE *stands poised, her hands over her head, clicking castanets. At a signal from* ALEC *the* MEN *in the corner burst out and drag* JACK *from his chair.* THEY *strip him of his rags and dress him as a gypsy dancer. Then* THEY *stand him next to* MARIA *and retreat to the corner, giving forth a few cries of "Fwed! Fwed!"*

MARIA *(Ecstatically)* Eeeeeeeeeyah! *(*SHE *begins stamping one heel)*

ALEC Music! The dance!

The MUSICIANS *play gypsy music, again on the phonograph, only this time throwing themselves violently into their playing.* MARIA *dances wildly, twisting, moaning, screaming.* JACK, *after some hesitation and a few looks at* ALEC, *joins her and dances clumsily but furiously, once getting knocked down.*

MARIA *(Screaming)* Eeeeeeeeeeyah! Ola! Ola! Ola! Eeeeeeeeeeyah!

JACK *(With enthusiasm, but* HE *does not have the abandon)* Ola! . . . Ola!

The MUSICIANS *and* MARIA *reach a climax and, with much screaming and movement, stop.* MARIA *runs out.*

ALEC *(Clapping)* You were splendid, Fred, splendid. I was completely taken in by you. You are a gypsy at heart. Deep down in you, you have romance. Sit down by me.

MEN Fwed! Fwed!

ALEC You see, my boy. You've pleased them. You're going to *win.*

JACK Win what?

ALEC Precisely. Will you have another drink?

JACK *(Timidly)* Could I eat?

ALEC *(Laughing)* Of course, of course. The dancing. My boy, don't be shy. We love you here. *(*HE *claps his hands)* Next act! Next!

The MEN *swarm over* JACK *again, this time dressing him in diapers and a baby hat.* THEY *leave him standing on the floor with a rattle.* MARIA, *looking pregnant, runs out in a flowery maternity dress and sits by the* MUSICIANS, *who take off their moustaches, untie their bandannas, and fasten their shirts.*

JACK Aren't we going to eat?

ALEC Soon, my boy, soon.

One of the MUSICIANS *takes a pump, attaches it to* MARIA*'s bosom and begins pumping. Her breasts swell up and finally burst out of her dress.* HE *continues pumping until they are enormous.*

Splendid, splendid. Now, Fred, sit in her lap.

JACK No. I won't do it. No, I've had enough of this.

The mumbling in the corner begins to rise.

I won't. . .

Cries of "Fwed! Fwed!"

do it. *(*HE *sits in* MARIA*'s lap)*

ALEC Now cuddle down.

JACK *looks imploringly at* ALEC.

I said cuddle down!

JACK *cuddles down.*

MARIA *(In a sweet baby voice)* Little baby hungry? Little baby want a drink? Oh, Mummy all so achy.

ALEC Say goo.

MARIA *(Tickling* JACK *under the chin)* Kitchi-kitchi-kitchi.

ALEC Say goo, you fool!

JACK Goo.

MARIA *(Hugging him to her breast)* Oh, you sweet thing! *(Rubbing her breasts)* Mummy so achy. Baby want a drink of milki?

JACK Goo. Goo, goo.

ALEC Splendid.

MARIA Take your milki now.

SHE *pushes* JACK*'s face into her breast and* HE *drinks.*

JACK *(Gagging)* Umm! Ummm!

ALEC To the last drop! It's all part of the show!

The MUSICIANS *play "Rock-a-bye, Baby" and* MARIA *hums. As* JACK *drinks,* MARIA*'s breasts shrink until they look like two deflated, wrinkled balloons. At the end, the music stops with a scratch, and* MARIA *unceremoniously drops* JACK *to the floor and rushes out. The* MEN *rush out, and hug* JACK*, crying "Fwed! Fwed!" When* THEY *leave him,* HE *is dressed in a striped pajama top and a hula skirt.*

JACK *(Looking at himself and realizing that he is in for something extraordinary)* Wah! Wah!

ALEC *(In his western drawl)* Okay, pardner, let's eat. I'm so hongry I could eat a hoss back end forwards. Har, har, har.

MARIA *runs out in a short frisky waitress costume and guides* JACK *to the table.*

MARIA Time to eat, sir. *(Covertly)* Psst! Psst! I'll see you later. Wait for me.

ALEC Come, my boy.

JACK *sits. The* MEN *in the corner come and hover around him, watching his every movement intensely.*

CROWS Guark! Guark! Guark!

ALEC Well now, Fred, how do you like our little town? Not so bad, eh?

JACK No. Oh, no. It's, it's—

ALEC A bit of all right, eh?

JACK It's a swell little town.

ALEC Listen. You know, Maria's a bit of a town whore, you know.

MARIA *giggles.*

You'll sleep with her later, eh?

JACK *looks at* MARIA. SHE *puts her finger to her lips, slowly slips it in her mouth, then pulls it out again.*

MARIA *(Whispering conspiratorially)* Play along. I'll speak to you later. We've got to get away!

JACK *(Nodding dumbly)* Uh.

MARIA *(With Hungarian accent)* You vant pretzel, baby? *(*SHE *giggles and pulls one out from under her dress. Then, whispering)* Don't let on that you know.

MEN Fwed! Fwed! *(THEY mumble contentedly)*

ALEC *(Pounding the table)* The food! Where's the food? Excuse me. *(HE gets up and goes out one of the doors)*

CROWS Guark! Guark! Guark!

MARIA *(When she sees he is gone)* Psst! Psst! *(JACK bends close)* You vant pretzel? . . . *(SHE laughs wildly, then stops abruptly)* Shhh! Take me away! Take me away! *(Shaking him frantically)* You've got to take me away!

JACK What?

MARIA Take me away!

JACK *(Nodding)* Don't they hear you? Aren't you afraid they'll hear you?

The eyes of the MEN are intent on them.

MARIA The hell with them! You've got to take me away! Don't you see what you've gotten into? What are you, a man or a mouse?

JACK *(Desperately)* Yes! Yes! I *want* to get away. But I'm afraid they'll kill me. You heard what Alec said. What's the matter with them? Are they crazy?

MARIA Bah! Don't you love me?

JACK Well . . . yes. I mean, I do like you.

MARIA *(Seductively, lifting her dress)* You vant pretzel, baby?

JACK Be serious. We're in a terrible fix.

SHE slaps him. HE begins to protest.

MARIA Swine! You saw my father out there?

JACK *(Shocked)* Your father! You mean—

MARIA *(Seductively)* You vant pretzel, baby?

JACK Will you be *serious?* How can I get away? Tell me how!

MARIA *(Slapping him again and grabbing him roughly by the hair)* Tonight ve make love. Tomorrow ve go away. Yes?

MEN *(Reaching out and touching* JACK*)* Fwed! Fwed!

ALEC *returns, sees what* THEY *are doing, and snaps his whip at them.* THEY *lower their hands but remain stationed just behind* JACK.

ALEC It's all right.

HE *claps his hands. A* WAITER *brings out two frankfurters.*

Don't worry, my boy. You'll love it. Chicken head and skunk cabbage roulade. That's the Monte Waite style. We make everything that way, you know. Good publicity. Oh, incidentally, I assumed you would like it very rare. To keep the juices, you know.

JACK Oh, yes. Certainly.

ALEC *(Violently)* Eat!

JACK *begins nibbling on a piece of frankfurter.* ALEC *eats heartily.*

Tell me now, Fred, what do you *really* think of our little community?

MARIA *kneels down by* JACK *as he nibbles.*

JACK Well . . . it certainly is . . . has . . .

ALEC Doesn't it? Did you notice the water pump in the square?

JACK No.

ALEC Why not?

JACK Well, I don't know. I just didn't.

ALEC *stares at him.* MARIA *strokes his legs.*

ALEC *(Laughing insanely)* Because it isn't there yet, that's why! *(*HE *laughs again, then stops abruptly)* But it's new, you know.

MARIA Psst. You vant pretzel? Take pretzel, baby. Plenty pretzel.

SHE *begins to cling more tightly to* JACK. HE *shakes his leg.*

ALEC Are your parents alive?

JACK Yes. They are. I come from a long-lived family.

ALEC *smiles.*

I mean . . . yes . . . they are.

ALEC And your first taste of sex? When was that? In the toilet? In the locker room?

JACK Certainly not.

ALEC When, then?

JACK *(Laughing awkwardly)* Well, you know how it is.

ALEC How?

JACK Well, I mean . . . Hell, I guess I was . . . fifteen?

ALEC Nothing earlier?

JACK Well, if you want to be a stickler. I was pretty—

MARIA *pinches him.*

Ow! I mean . . . *(Whispering)* Cut it out.

SHE *giggles.*

ALEC And what was her name?

JACK *(After a pause)* Lulu. *(Silence)* She was a Baptist.

ALEC Is there any cancer in your family?

JACK Cancer?

ALEC Yes. Cancer. Carcinoma. That disease that eats away the healthy body until only death can survive.

JACK Well, I don't know. I don't think so. Why?

ALEC Wouldn't you like to know?

JACK *(A little belligerently, annoyed at the questions)* Well, yes, I would, I suppose. There's too goddam much I don't know already.

ALEC Is that a pointed remark, Fred?

JACK *(Laughing nervously)* No, no. Why do you think that?

ALEC *(Sternly)* Remember you are our guest.

MARIA *hugs* JACK*'s arm.*

Now then, did you ever wet your bed?

JACK No.

ALEC Were you an asset to the community?

JACK I certainly was. I was treasurer of the G.O. in high school, if that's what you mean.

ALEC It is.

JACK And now I'm a member of the Caribou.

ALEC Oh? The Caribou? (HE *laughs in contempt)*

JACK It's a *very* charitable organization. They do a lot of *good things.* I'm *proud* to be a Caribou. (JACK, *as if inspired, looks up a moment, then crosses his arms and waves his hands in the air, emitting a long caribou call. This seems to give him confidence)*

ALEC Ingenious. I'm very impressed, my boy.

JACK Well, you ought to be. The Caribous are a very powerful organization.

ALEC Did your grandfather vote for Wilson?

JACK No. I mean I don't know.

ALEC Was your mother a virgin when she married?

JACK Now see here. I've—

ALEC Tut, tut, tut. You really needn't answer that one.

JACK Well, I certainly won't.

ALEC Last year we planted maples in the square.

JACK If a man's mother isn't sacred, then I— Why, that's the fifth oath of the Caribous.

ALEC To give the old folks a shady spot.

JACK My mother was a wonderful women.

ALEC But we really don't have that many old people.

JACK My father adored her. She was the apple of his eye.

ALEC Did they sleep together? Was she a virgin when you were born?

JACK *(Speechless)* What-what-what kind of question is that? Of course they did. *(A little shocked at what* HE *has said)* But, but . . . I mean . . . I never actually *saw* them. *(*HE *stops speaking, a puzzled look on his face)*

ALEC Were you ever left back in school?

JACK Certainly not.

ALEC Was there any idiocy in your family?

JACK Certainly not.

ALEC *(Mocking)* Certainly not. Certainly not. You're pretty smug, aren't you, Fred? *(*HE *pauses, then stands up suddenly. In his Indian voice)* White man, you die!

HE *pulls out a gun, presses it to* JACK*'s head, and fires as* JACK *screams. The gun pops like a toy gun, and* ALEC *laughs.*

You see how easy it would be? Nothing. Nothing at all.

MARIA *begins kissing* JACK *on the face and neck.*

I said you were smug, Fred. Did you hear me?

JACK What do you mean?

ALEC I mean these poor souls *(*HE *motions to the* MEN *behind* JACK*)* have been waiting for years for you to arrive, and here you—

JACK I *tried* to tell you that my name isn't—

ALEC Tut, tut, tut. Will never do. What's in a name, Fred? Umm? Be careful, young man. They're capable of anything. Even eating you alive. Now, let me—

JACK Hah! Well, I don't care if they are. And just what is it this Fred is supposed to do anyway. Listen, I'm getting *fed up.* You can do your damnedest, but I'm through. *(*HE *stands up)*

ALEC You mean you don't know what you're supposed to do?

JACK No. And what's more I don't . . .

The MEN *all take out long knives and moan "Fwed! Fwed!"* JACK *sits down slowly.*

. . . care. I mean, well . . . no. Not really. I mean . . . all you do is keep saying they're waiting for this Fred.

ALEC For you.

JACK *(Weakly)* For me. But . . . well . . . what for?

ALEC Ah.

JACK Gee whiskers, is that all you have to say?

ALEC For the time being. Any more Caribou in you?

JACK *(Reviving a little)* Damn right.

ALEC Any more questions?

JACK *(Pushing* MARIA *away, gently but firmly)* I guess I could ask you a few good ones.

ALEC Shoot, pardner.

JACK Who are you?

ALEC No comment. I am a mystery.

JACK What's going on here.

ALEC No comment. The celebration is immaterial.

JACK Who's Fred?

ALEC You, my boy.

JACK *(After a pause)* What do you want with him?

ALEC His blood. *(*HE *lets out a wild, shrieking laugh)*

JACK *(Jumping up and turning over his chair)* That's not very funny.

ALEC I assure you, it isn't funny at all. *(Claps his hands)* Knives away, boys, knives away.

The MEN *put their knives away.*

JACK I'm getting out of here if I have to crawl.

ALEC And if you can't crawl?—Oh, let's not bicker. Wait. *(Silence)* Ha ha! The colors.

FOUR MEN *march by, one holding a flag, one playing a drum, one playing a fife, one walking a dog. The tune is "Yankee Doodle."* ALEC *holds his hand over his heart.* JACK *salutes, gives the Caribou call, and, when* THEY *leave, stands a little uncertainly.*

I'm glad you're a patriot, my boy. The land needs patriots. And now I think you'd better go to bed. I did promise you a little fun, didn't I?

MARIA *giggles.*

*(*ALEC *shouts)* Night! Night!

The lights go out immediately. There is a moon. Only JACK *and* MARIA *are visible in the dim flicker of light. The heads of a few* MEN *cast shadows.*

MARIA Oh, Fred. The hour is ours at last. *(Whispering)* Psst! I know you're not really Fred.

JACK Oh, thank God!

MARIA You're George.

JACK *laughs hysterically.*

Hush. Hush, my darling. We have to play the game. We really do, Fred. *(*SHE *giggles and runs away)*

JACK Maria. Come back. . . . Where are you?

MARIA *(Giggling; she is across the stage, sitting at a dressing table, wearing a filmy nightgown and combing her hair)* In a moment, my darling. I want to be beautiful for you. Perfectly beautiful.

*(*SHE *sprays herself with an old-fashioned insect spray)* This is our night.

JACK *(Coming to her)* Tell me how to get out of here. Now! You said you would. What do I smell?

MARIA *(Swinging around and laughing in a sultry Hungarian voice)* Oh, you are funny boy. *(*SHE *runs giggling to the bar)* Quick. Quick. You help poor gypsy girl, eh? *(*SHE *pulls out a bed and jumps in, twisting and groaning)* Ah, Freddie, you are funny boy.

SHE *laughs. The lights dim so that* THEY *are barely visible.*

Now big hug for gypsy girl, eh? Come. Come. *(*SHE *moans)* Ahhh . . . better. Better. *(*SHE *laughs again)* Is not so hard, eh? Now, ve do business?

JACK *groans.*

Noooo? Funny boy! You like gypsy girl? You like tricks? Eh? Oh! *(*SHE *screams and laughs)* You are naughty boy . . . Is good no lights, eh? . . . I bet you blush, eh? You like gypsy tricks?

JACK *groans.*

Gypsy girl is good, no? *(*SHE *laughs)* You vant more gypsy trick? Eh? You vant big pretzel?

JACK *(Thickly)* What's that noise?

There is a shuffling of feet and low mumbling.

MARIA That?

JACK Yes.

Gradually the heads of the MEN *become visible just behind them.* THEY *watch wide-eyed.* JACK *suddenly notices them, stifles a shriek, and sits up.*

MARIA Shhh! Don't pay any attention to them. They'll rip you to pieces in a second. Their fingers are claws. Make believe they're not there. *Pretend!*

JACK *(Whispering)* But they *are* there!

MARIA *(Laughing in a low voice)* You like gypsy girl? You like gypsy trick? Eh? Ve make more gypsy trick? *(Whispering)* For God's sake, play along! Don't you want to get out of this? Do you want them to kill me?

JACK I've got to urinate. It's coming.

MARIA *(Matter-of-factly)* Down the hall, buster.

JACK *fumbles out of bed. As* HE *does, the light fades by the bar and brightens in the middle of the room, though not very much.* HARRINGTON, *a man dressed in animal skins, sits on a rock by a fire.* HE *is making rather tuneless music by blowing through a wooden tube with his nose. Ashes fall throughout the scene. Tinny drumbeats in the distance. There is a vague outline of burned buildings and some odd scaffoldings. What looks like the prow of a large canoe juts out of the darkness. Mounted on it is a large painted and sculptured head. Mobiles of stumps and charred, shapeless objects hang from the sky.*

JACK *(Noticing* THE MAN*)* Oh . . . I'm looking for the bathroom.

HARRINGTON *(With an English accent)* Over there, old bean.

JACK *walks several paces, sees nothing, stops.*

That's it. You can unload right there. I say, have we met?

JACK *(Walking back)* Well, no. I don't think so. I'm Jack—

HARRINGTON Right. Harrington's the name. Charmed to meet you, dear chap. *(*HE *shakes his hand heartily)* Have a sit, won't you?

THEY *sit on two rocks.*

New, aren't you?

JACK Yes.

HARRINGTON I say, would you help us? Be frightfully good of you.

JACK Well, if I can.

HARRINGTON Splendid. Have you eaten? We're about due for tea.

JACK What do you want me to do?

HARRINGTON Oh, just kill a few blokes. Bash them, you know. Frightful blighters. Been stepping across the line, don't you know. They've got their own lot, but they don't want to stick it. Damned *nouveaux riches.* Can't have that, you know. We've got to observe the boundaries. Tradition and all that rot. Don't you agree?

JACK *(Warily)* Yes.

HARRINGTON You see, I'd like to get them buried, what's left of them, before the weekend. Guests, you know. The Duchess of Wherry's coming. And Sir Charles—great sport, he is. Simply mad for grouse. And, oh, dear, Mother said she'd come if the temperature rose. Say, why don't you stay? *Lots* of tennis. Lawn of course.

JACK I don't . . . play.

HARRINGTON You don't play tennis? . . . Bridge?

JACK No. I was just going to the bathroom.

HARRINGTON *(Suspiciously)* No? No tennis, no bridge? I say, where did you say you came from?

A CROWD *of men and women, shouting, all dressed in skins, suddenly swoop around them, apparently trying to catch something in their midst.* THEY *move away as suddenly as they came.*

Jolly good fun. Where were we, old bean?

JACK I was looking for the bathroom.

HARRINGTON But didn't you just unload?

JACK No. I couldn't find the bathroom.

HARRINGTON *(Laughing loudly)* Good joke! I like you!

A YOUNG GIRL *appears at the edge of the fire and stands coyly looking at her feet.*

Oh, Sybil, there you are. My daughter, you know. She's coming out next week. Regular feast we're having.

SYBIL *flings herself across* JACK*'s legs and begins writhing.*

Oh, don't mind her. Playful as a kitten. Give her a buss or two. That's what she wants, you know.

In the distance we hear SOMEONE *scream horribly, then cheers. Shadows from a fire flicker across the stage as the yelling continues.* SYBIL *twists and turns in* JACK*'s lap, purring loudly.*

My dear fellow, you've made quite a hit. We may have to pair you off. She's young, but quite effective. *(Chuckling to himself)* Oh, quite. But she likes to be treated a little rough. Cuff her about a bit, you know. Bite her nooky. Mind, she'll bite back. But it's all jolly clean fun. What?

JACK *(Timidly)* Ha ha. Do you think I might go to the bathroom now?

HARRINGTON *(Laughing loudly)* I say! Mother's going to love you! Rum fellow!

JACK I really have to go.

HARRINGTON *(With menace)* I say, you don't want it to get stale, do you. Try another, that's a good chap.

JACK I left a girl in bed back—

HARRINGTON *(Laughing loudly)* Rum go! Rum go! You *are* a dear chap!

HE *suddenly knocks* SYBIL *off* JACK*'s lap.*

Don't forget your manners, dear. Get the fellow some eats for tea.

SYBIL *tries to claw him, but* HE *knocks her down again.* SHE *scurries off.*

Great spirit she's got, don't you think? Good lines. Thoroughbred, you know. Take a peek at her flanks when she returns. Her mother was a Fleetwood. Finest haunch in the Empire. Damned sorry to see her go, poor girl. But she put up a good fight.

THEY *stare at each other a minute.* THE STATE TROOPER *rides by slowly.*

So you don't play bridge?

JACK No.

HARRINGTON See here, where'd you say you went to school?

JACK Well, I graduated from Dudley College.

HARRINGTON Dudley College?

JACK I majored in business management.

HARRINGTON Is that in Wales or something?

JACK No, it's in Dudleyville.

HARRINGTON Dudleyville?

JACK Yes. You see, Maynard Dudley made a fortune in chocolates. The Dudley Bar? . . . It's world famous. And he left his money for Dudley College. He's buried there, so they call the town Dudleyville.

HARRINGTON *(Suspiciously)* I see.

JACK I grew up in Dudleyville. My father was the caretaker there for fifty years. And I got tuition free.

HARRINGTON I see. You don't have any of these . . . Dudley Bars on you, do you?

JACK No.

HARRINGTON I see.

JACK Now may I go and urinate?

SYBIL *returns carrying several wet, slippery pieces of flesh.* HARRINGTON *grabs one and begins eating voraciously.* SYBIL *throws one to* JACK, *then begins eating her own.* JACK *looks at the meat in horror.*

HARRINGTON Eat the damn thing!

SYBIL *watches* JACK. HE *takes token bites, suddenly turns and vomits.*

I say, you're not one of them, are you?

JACK *(White and frightened)* No! No!

HARRINGTON I think you are.

JACK No. I just wanted to urinate.

HARRINGTON I'm sure you are. I should have known.

SYBIL *begins stroking* JACK *with a hungry look.*

JACK No! Leave me alone! I tell you no!

THE OTHERS *gather round, some of them still eating wet slippery pieces of meat.*

HARRINGTON I say, chaps, I think he's one of them.

THEY *close in on* JACK, *growling.*

JACK No! No! No!

As THEY *close in on him, the light fades.* JACK *screams. A sudden brilliant, blinding flash of light. The drums become louder, then stop. Complete darkness. Silence. Then a pale light over the bed.*

MARIA Funny boy. What for you scare gypsy girl, huh? You vant make gypsy love again, huh? You vant play tricks?

JACK *(Desperately)* No. Oh, God, get me out of here!

MARIA Here, funny boy. You take like . . . so. Nice? Yah? You like? . . . Gypsy girl is different, eh? *(*SHE *laughs)* Hongry boy! *(*SHE *laughs again)* Is old gypsy trick.

JACK *moans. Suddenly the lights go on, revealing them in bed with* THE MEN *clustering behind them.* ALEC *enters, stands facing them ominously.*

ALEC I forgot to say goodnight. *(*HE *pauses)* Goodnight.

HE *leaves. The lights go out again.*

JACK Listen. *(Desperately)* I want to get away! I want to get away! Do you understand? I'll do anything! I'll run away with you! Anything! Anything!

MARIA Ohhhh. You don't like gypsy girl? You don't like gypsy trick?

JACK *(Shouting)* Listen to me!

MARIA *(Whispering)* Shhhh! Don't let them hear you. They'll kill me. Do you hear? They'll kill me! Don't you *care* about me? Take me with you! You've got to take me with you!—

JACK *(Screaming)* All right! For God's sake, all right!

MARIA Psst! Psst!

JACK What?

MARIA Ve make gypsy love, huh? Ve make gypsy trick? Huh? *(Whispering)* You've got to take me with you!

JACK *(Frenzied)* Just tell me *how! (*HE *giggles hysterically)*

A line of BALLERINAS *from Swan Lake, all in white, shivers diagonally across the room to the tremor of violins.*

MARIA Shhhh.

JACK Wha—?

MARIA The hour before the dawn.

JACK Huh?

MARIA The hour before the dawn.

Suddenly, the sound of a shade being let up. Bright daylight. THE MEN *retreat, break up into friendly groups at the tables and talk normally.* ALEC *enters smartly.*

ALEC *(Cheerfully)* Morning, morning. Another day. I hope you enjoyed your rest? Eggs and bacon all right for breakfast?

MARIA Oh, my God. I've got to get dressed.

SHE *leaps out of bed, ducks behind the bar and puts on her waitress uniform.* JACK *sits on the edge of the bed somewhat dazed.*

ALEC Breakfast in ten minutes, sir.

MARIA *(Giggling)* Eggs and bacon, sir?

JACK All right.

MARIA Sunny-side? *(*SHE *giggles)*

JACK Basted.

MARIA *giggles and runs off.*

ALEC *(Handing* JACK *clothes)* Let me help you.

JACK *dresses.*

Good news, good news, sir.

JACK What?

ALEC Your car.

JACK Yes?

ALEC It's fixed. You'll be on your way after breakfast.

JACK *(Almost pleading)* You're not joking?

ALEC Sir. Why should I joke? I think I know my place.

JACK It's fixed?

ALEC The mechanic will give you a personal report himself shortly.

JACK Oh.

ALEC *(Winking)* Did you sleep well, sir? We try to provide every comfort.

JACK I, I . . . had some dreams.

ALEC Dreams?

JACK Yes . . . dreams.

ALEC Perhaps it was something you ate. Did you like our . . . little entertainment? Our . . . show?

JACK Show?

ALEC Yes. Our show. We put on a pretty fine one, if I do say so.

JACK *(Grasping at straws)* You mean . . . It was all . . . ?

ALEC Indeed I do. Did you like it?

JACK *(Smiling with relief, almost unable to believe in his good fortune)* Well . . . a show. God. *(*HE *laughs in relief)* A show. You certainly . . .

ALEC *(Eagerly)* You liked it? Tell me you liked it. The performers will be so pleased.

JACK *(Emphatically)* It was sensational! A smash! A knockout!

ALEC *(Beside himself, running back and forth)* Oh, splendid. Wonderful. You don't know how much this means to us. Crows. Oh, crows.

THE CROWS *come out, smiling.* THEY *greet* JACK *and* HE *compliments them.* THEY *sit at a table.*

Tumblers! Oh, where are they?

THE TUMBLERS *run out and shake hands with* JACK, *then sit at a table.*

Musicians! Musicians! Forward now.

THE MUSICIANS *come out and bow formally to* JACK. HE *returns the bow.*

Now, breakfast. You've made us so happy.

JACK *(Looking around)* Where are the others?

ALEC *(Puzzled)* The others?

JACK The, the . . .

ALEC Oh, you mean the boys.

HE *waves his hand to* THE MEN, *now sitting at the tables.* THEY *look up, smile at* JACK, *wave. A few of them say "Hi, Jack."*

JACK They called me Jack.

ALEC Of course they did. That's your name, isn't it?

JACK *(Looking uncertain for a moment)* It sure is.

ALEC Maria!

MARIA *runs out with* JACK*'s breakfast tray.* SHE *sets it on the table and curtsies.*

JACK I'm starving.

ALEC Eat heartily, sir. We want you to have only the best memories of Monte Waite.

JACK *begins eating hungrily as* ALEC *and* MARIA *watch him indulgently.* ALEC *winks at* MARIA. SHE *blushes.*

I'm sorry your dinner didn't agree with you last night. I'm sure you won't have trouble with your breakfast.

JACK *(His mouth stuffed)* Ummmmm-uh.

ALEC Did you have everything you needed last night?

JACK *(Hastily swallowing his food)* Well, you know, I got up once to go to the bathroom and I met the damnedest—

ALEC You got up?

JACK Yes. I had to go to the bathroom and—

ALEC How long were you gone?

JACK Well, that's just it, you see. I—

ALEC How long?

JACK Well, I guess about half an hour.

ALEC *(Furiously)* You were gone half an hour?

JACK Well, it was only half an hour.

ALEC *Only* half an hour! . . . *(Laughs bitterly)* Then you missed part of the show.

JACK Well, that's all right. Honest. I got plenty. Maria more than made up for . . . *(*HE *laughs)* Well, you know how it is.

ALEC *(Walking back and forth angrily)* I cannot allow it! The penultimate act! I will not tolerate it! No! *(Smacking the back of one hand into the palm of the other)* No! No!

JACK Hey. Take it easy. Don't get so worked up. I don't care. It's all right with me.

ALEC *(Turning on him suddenly)* Yes. Precisely. *You* don't care. *(*HE *pauses)* But *I* do. *(*HE *walks briskly to the bar, takes out his whip and begins snapping it at* THE MEN*)* Back! Back!

MEN *(Shuffling to the corner)* Fwed! Fwed!

JACK Hey. Wait, now. I—

ALEC Out! Out!

THE MUSICIANS *and* TUMBLERS *run out.*

Maria!

MARIA *is already undressing and jumping into bed.*

Crows! Crows! Get up! Get up!

THE CROWS *perch on the trapeze.*

CROWS Guark! Guark! Guark!

ALEC And you, my boy. You fool! You unmitigated, innocent fool! You flabby, arrogant, deluded creature! We shall pull out your tongue with fishhooks and horses. We shall stuff your mouth with the excrement of bilious old men!

HE *snaps his whip at* JACK, *forcing him back to the bed.*

Get in there! Quick!

JACK *scrambles over the bed, thoroughly frightened.*

Lights! *(Screaming)* LIGHTS!

The lights fade. The mumbling MEN *shuffle near the bed.*

THUNDER! THUNDER! NIGHT! DARKNESS!

HE *laughs loudly, demonically. Throughout the scene, rain, loud thunder, lightning.*

MARIA Ve make gypsy love? Hey. Funny boy. You like gypsy trick?

JACK *(Crying hysterically)* No! No! No! No! I want to get out of here! I want to get out of here! I want to go home!

MEN Fwed! Fwed!

MARIA Shhh! Don't let them hear you. Don't let them know you're afraid. They can smell it. They'll stick forks in you. That's the way they begin.

JACK *(Exhausted with fear)* I want to get out of here. Oh, I want to get out of here. *(Crying again)* Please. You, you, you—

MARIA *(Solacing him)* I show you special gypsy trick. Only Maria know special gypsy trick. Funny boy.

Just before the light fades completely, the same line of BALLERINAS, *all in white, shivers diagonally across the stage to the tremor of violins. In the far corner a pale red light comes up slowly.*

JACK *(Pleading)* What's going to happen now?

MARIA The Moke-Eater.

JACK What's that?

MARIA The Moke-Eater. She is the end.

A FIGURE *drags itself into the red light. It can vaguely be recognized as the figure of the* OLD MAN *seen earlier in the street.* HE *pulls himself onto a table and with much effort attains a kneeling position.*

JACK Your father! That's your father!

MARIA Shhh! Be still, you fool!

After the FIGURE *has been kneeling for a minute, an amorphous* FORM *slowly moves out of the shadows towards him.* IT *moves directly up to him and seems to be pushing him in the stomach. The lightning gives only momentary vision that is never sufficient. Sounds of animal eating. The* OLD MAN*'s moans, which gradually become louder and more painful expressions of the* *greatest agony, mingle with the thunder. At the height of his torment, the red light fades slowly until it is completely dark. Silence.*

JACK Oh, God, hold me! Hold me! Maria!

MARIA *(Crying)* Take me away! You must take me away! You must!

THEY *embrace.*

JACK Maria!

Suddenly the lights go on again. It is daytime. ALEC *enters, smiling. The* CROWS, MUSICIANS, TUMBLERS, *and* MEN *are all sitting sociably at the tables.*

ALEC There we are. That's all. Get up now, you slug-abed lovers.

MARIA *giggles and jumps out of bed, dressing again in her waitress uniform.*

Jack, I can't tell you what a pleasure it has been having you.

JACK *gets up slowly, avoiding* ALEC.

You've been simply splendid. Sit down. Have your coffee. Your car will be ready in a jiffy.

JACK *sits and takes small sips of coffee.*

How do you feel?

JACK *(Nervously)* Okay. Okay. *(*HE *will believe nothing now)*

ALEC Splendid. And did you like our little show?

JACK It was okay.

ALEC Ohh. Only okay?

JACK *(Deadpan)* It was great. Just great.

MECHANIC *(Entering)* Howdy, Mister Jack.

JACK H-h-hello.

MECHANIC Fixed 'er real good. Humming like a bird, she is.

JACK I can go?

MECHANIC Why, sure thing. Any time you like.

ALEC *(To the* MECHANIC*)* Coffee?

MECHANIC Nope. Et already. Have a good trip now. Stop by again, hear?

JACK Yes. Yes, I'll do that.

The MECHANIC *leaves.*

ALEC Darn nice feller.

JACK Yes.

ALEC It's a wonderful town, Jack. Worse places a feller could settle. Fishing? Superb. Nicest folk you'd want to meet.

JACK *(Laughing awkwardly)* I'm sure of it.

ALEC Pity you ain't met more of the women folk. They're real special. *(*HE *waits for* JACK *to respond, then continues)* No, sir. Never regretted a moment of it. Never a moment. Wife wouldn't think of leaving.

JACK You're married?

JACK Married! Six kids!

JACK Six?

ALEC Yep.

JACK How—how old?

ALEC Well . . . lemme see—*(*HE *counts his fingers)*

MAN *(Shouting from a table)* You got seven now, Alec. You lost count?

THE MEN *laugh good-naturedly.*

ALEC By God, I do. Darned if he ain't right. I clean forgot little Mandy. But then, she's so durn tiny.

JACK *(Trying to leave)* Well, it was a good breakfast. Thanks for the, the show and everything.

ALEC We do our best in Monte Waite.

JACK Will you take my Diner's Card for everything?

ALEC Yep. Sure will.

JACK *takes out a pack of cards and gives* ALEC *one.* ALEC *leaves. While he is gone,* JACK *looks at* MARIA, *who is leaning across the counter looking at him.* HE *conspicuously takes out several bills and lays them on the table. Then* HE *takes another one out and puts it down.* SHE *giggles.* HE *smiles at her and waves awkwardly.*

JACK *(Still waving)* Bye. Bye-bye.

SHE *giggles and looks at the counter.* HE *kisses the air several times.* ALEC *returns and gives* JACK *his card.*

ALEC I took out for the car, too.

JACK Fine.

ALEC Fine.

JACK Well, can I go now?

ALEC Why sure you can.

JACK Well. Good-bye, then. Thanks.

ALEC You have yourself a good trip now. And come back again soon.

JACK Well, I'll try.

ALEC Can't ask a man to do more than that.

JACK *(Waving in general)* Well, bye now.

EVERYONE *in the bar smiles and waves at him.* THEY *follow him out and stand on the porch as* HE *waves to the people outside and walks off, a little too quickly. Sound of car door opening, then slamming. The motor starts.* EVERYONE *waves and shouts "Bye!" The car moves off, at first slowly, then more quickly. The sound fades. As it does,* ALEC, MARIA, *and all* THE OTHERS *return to the bar and remain frozen in their attitudes.* THE CROWS *get on their trapeze. Outside, the scene is the same as at the beginning of the play. The* STATE TROOPER *rides through slowly. Silence. This lasts a minute. Suddenly a door in the back of the bar opens.* JACK *enters, talking as he walks in.*

JACK Say, I hope you folks can help me. My car—

HE *stops as he realizes where he is. His entrance has released everyone into movement.* THEY *turn and stare at him.*

But . . . I can't be here. I left here three hours ago. *(*HE *shakes his head)* I left here. Th-th-this is all a mistake. It's a mistake.

ALEC *giggles viciously as a background to* JACK*'s bewildered pleas.*

I left here. I tell you I left here. Maria!

SHE *giggles.*

CROWS Guark! Guark! Guark!

JACK But I did. I did leave here.

The MEN *begin shuffling toward him slowly.*

I did.

The bright lights dim. A pale red light slowly showers the bar, gradually diminishing in area until only JACK, *then his head, is visible in it.* HE *looks at the audience.*

I left here, I tell you. I left here. *(Shouting)* I tell you I left here!

Complete silence. For half a minute HE *stares at the audience with terror-stricken eyes. Then sudden and complete blackness.*

MARY JANE
A Monologue

The stage is dark. Sound of heavy traffic; siren in distance, which gradually diminishes. A light is turned on stage center, directly over table. Sitting leaning at the table, a MAN *in his late fifties, gaunt, nearly toothless, shabby, a little wild-looking. The room is small and dirty. A dilapidated bed in shadow. Newspapers peeling from the walls. The corners dark. Nothing else in the room is visible. The* MAN *is staring without expression at the audience. The only thing on the table is a broken-down radio.* HE *snorts a few times from the glare of the light, wipes his mouth, scratches his head, and looks at the audience a long time. Then, as if snapping out of something:*

MAN Well, well, well, well.

HE *shifts his chair, looks around the table as if uncertain what to do, finally tries the radio in a few positions, settles on one, and looks at it a while.*

Uh-huh.

HE *brushes the radio off with his hand, blows a little dust away, then looks around, folds his hands, and looks at the audience.* HE *breaks his stare several times to blow specks of dust off the table.* HE *has no expression. Then, as if discovering something,* HE *holds up his fingers.*

Ahhhh.

HE *looks at the audience again, a faint smile on his face; gets up abruptly, looks around, goes to an invisible sink and gets a glass of water.* HE *returns to the table, takes out a handkerchief, and wipes the glass.* HE *puts it down carefully and looks at it, changes its position several times until he is satisfied, then adjusts the radio in relation to the glass. With a lot of clatter,* HE *sits down, draws his chair close to the table, then pushes it back, reaches in his pocket, brings out a crumpled sandwich in cellophane, and noisily draws himself close to the table again, placing the sandwich down with a firm gesture.* HE *sniffs, then laughs.*

Ha, ha! There, now.

HE *snorts several times.*

Yes, there we are. Pretty as a picture. Ha, ha!

HE *slaps his hand on the table in a gesture of finality and sits looking at the food.* HE *pulls out a watch, giggles, places it carefully on the table, looks around pleased, then frowns and looks at the watch again.* HE *picks it up and listens.*

Ah ah! That's the ticket. Yesssss, that's the ticket.

With a triumphant flourish, HE *turns on the radio and looks happily at the audience. His expression gradually fades as nothing happens. Suddenly* HE *pounds the radio in a rage. Static, then a voice.*

RADIO . . . with rain. Wednesday less cloudy with patches of sun, but cold and windy. *(Pause)* The time is now four fourteen and *(Pause)* thirty-two seconds. *(Static)*

MAN *(Slapping the table)* Hah!

RADIO You are listening to station—*(Static. The radio goes dead)*

HE *sets his watch but does not wind it. Putting it down carefully,* HE *rearranges the radio, the glass of water, and the sandwich.* HE *blows more dust away, brushes his pants, wipes his hands on his sweater, then rubs them together gleefully. Slowly* HE *unwraps the sandwich and, gazing abstractedly at a corner of the ceiling, eats it with large careful bites, moaning contentedly. Static, then a voice.*

RADIO . . . brutal murder. The body of the child was discovered at ten forty-two A.M. by the janitor of the building. Police say that this is the most vicious crime in memory. The girl, Mary Jane, to all appearances *(Static)* . . . a medical report. On the stock market, prices *(Static)* . . . wheat and *(Static. The radio goes dead)*

HE *pauses suddenly, as if struck by a thought. Then, looking at the audience,* HE *recites.*

MAN

What is the matter with Mary Jane?
She's perfectly well and she hasn't a pain,
And it's lovely rice pudding for dinner again!
What *is* the matter with Mary Jane?

HE *pauses, as if expecting some response, then laughs hysterically.*

RADIO The time is now four nineteen and *(Pause)* forty-seven seconds.

HE *stops laughing abruptly and looks disturbed. Slowly* HE *looks at his watch.*

MAN Hah!

HE *picks it up and resets the time, puts it down again, tilting his head with a click of satisfaction.* HE *picks up his water and gulps it down quickly to the last drop, then puts the glass down with firmness.*

Well! Hmmmmm.

HE *smacks his lips, then drums his fingers. Suddenly* HE *crumbles up the wrapping of his sandwich meticulously, opens a drawer in the table, drops the wrapping in, and slams the drawer shut.*

Well, to work, to work.

HE *feels all his pockets as if he has lost something. At last* HE *touches one, and pauses, gradually looking at the audience and smiling slyly.* HE *giggles and slowly pulls out a very worn letter, placing it carefully on the table, smoothing it out.* HE *pulls out rimless glasses, puts them on in a businesslike manner, and clears his throat for a minute. Then, with determination and visible but suppressed excitement,* HE *takes the letter out of the envelope, unfolds it, and holds it in front of him. Snorting:*

Dear Mr. Berger.

HE *stops, readjusts his chair, takes off his glasses, wipes them, puts them on again, clears his throat, and reads quickly.*

Dear Mr. Berger. This is to remind you that the check for your February telephone bill was $1.89 short. We are sure that this was simply an oversight, but as it is now May, we would greatly appreciate your rectifying it. Please let me know if we can be of further service. Yours truly, George B. Boone, Office of Accounts.

HE *pauses, puts the letter down, and appears to be thinking.*

Well, well, well, well.

HE *smacks his lips, adjusts his chair, and picks up the letter again, testing it at different lengths from his eyes.* HE *reads it again, changing his manner, tone, and inflection.*

Dear Mr. Berger. This is to remind you that the check for your February telephone bill was $1.89 short. We are sure that this is simply an oversight, but as it is now May, we would greatly appreciate your rectifying it. Please let me know if we can be of further service. Yours truly, George B. Boone, Office of Accounts.

HE *puts the letter down slowly and purses his lips.*

Well. That puts a different complexion on the matter. Entirely different complexion.

HE *drums his fingers on the table and squirms in his chair.* HE *rests both palms on the table as if to rise, but does not. Instead,* HE *begins the letter again, now quite angry.*

Dear Mr. Berger. This is to remind you—

HE *jumps up suddenly and walks back and forth as if perturbed.* HE *stops at the wall, pulls on his lower lip.*

Hmmmmm.

Something on the wall attracts his attention and HE *brings his face close. Then* HE *rips off a piece of newspaper and stares at it, reading with great difficulty in the dark.*

Bir-ke-nau. Bir-ke-nau. Bir-ke-nau. *(*HE *pauses, then passionately, feeling whiplashes as* HE *speaks) Yiden! Yiden!* Revolt! Do not listen to their promises! You will all be killed! *(Whispering) Yiden! Yiden!—*

HE *stops short, spits, jerks his head a few times, crumples the paper angrily and throws it down, snorting.* HE *returns to the table, as if with purpose, and sits down. Picking up the letter again,* HE *reads it through with still another change of manner, tone, and inflection:* Dear Mr. Berger. This is to remind you that the check for your February telephone bill was $1.89 short. We are sure that this was simply an oversight, but as it is now May, we would greatly appreciate your rectifying it. Please let me know if we can be of further service. Yours truly, George B. Boone, Office of Accounts.

HE *stares at the letter awhile, then throws it down on the table.*

No! No, no, no, no! It is a violation of the rights of man! It simply cannot be done! I have a *soul!*

HE *pounds his fist slowly on the table in controlled anger, then subsides into meditation. Slowly, as if he has thought about the matter considerably:*

Boone. George B. Boone. George B. Boone. *(Pause)* Benjamin? Boris? *(Pause)* George Boris Boone. Hmmmm. George Basil Boone! Hah! *(*HE *laughs)* Yes, Basil. I've got him, I've got him. Ha, ha! I've got you, George Basil Boone. By the tail!

HE *chuckles to himself, then stops abruptly.* HE *looks worried.*

Bruce? George Bruce Boone?

HE *shakes his head slowly and sinks into thought.*

Noooo. Noooo.

HE *is silent. Then jumping up:*

No!

HE *slaps the table.*

No! *Time is money.*

HE *stares at the audience.*

Time is money.

HE *ducks his head and snorts.* HE *folds up the letter quickly, puts it in the envelope, and slides it into his pocket. Then* HE *shuffles toward the bed, jerking his head. Static. A voice.*

RADIO . . . time is now five twenty-nine and *(Pause)* five seconds. *(Static)*

MAN *(Rushes back to the table and pounces on the watch)* Mmmmm . . . twenty-nine and five seconds. Hah!

HE *puts the watch down and chuckles.* HE *shuffles back to the bed and, with some effort, drags out an old telephone book, which* HE *brings back to the table.*

There now. Huh!

HE *rubs his hands and seats himself.*

Let me see. Hmmmm. Let me see.

HE *brings his head close to the cover.*

Detroit? Chicago? Noooo. No, no, no, no. Ah! *(*HE *looks up triumphantly, then hurriedly leafs through the pages)* Yesss . . . Hmmmmm. *(*HE *hums a few cheerful notes)*—"N"! *(*HE *looks up again triumphantly, then bends his head to the page)*

Noonan! That's it, "N"—Noonan. Fred C. Hah. *(*HE *chuckles)* Yes, there he is. Fred C. Noonan. Huh! Noonan, Gregory G. Well! Well, well, well, well. What have we here? Gregory Gregory Noonan? Hey? Hey?

HE *giggles wildly to himself.*

G.G. G.G. Noonan. He, he, he!

HE *takes out his handkerchief and wipes his nose.*

Enough frivolity. Frivolity. Oh, granny. Hmmmm. Well, every man his little jokes. Eh? Eh? Hmmmmph.

HE *bends over again.*

Noonan, John.

HE *shakes his head.*

Common. Very common. Noonan, Joseph J. Hmmmm. Not bad. J. J.? J. J. Noonan. Good. Good, good, good.

Static, then a voice:

RADIO . . . the heart-warming music of—

Static, then heart-warming music. HE *hits the radio angrily. More static. Another voice.*

. . . exactly six fifty-nine and *(Pause)* forty seconds.

A brief strain of music, then static, then the radio goes dead. HE *looks up from the telephone book.*

MAN Eh? Eh? Forty seconds? Hmmmph.

HE *grabs his watch and resets it.*

Hah! That's the ticket.

HE *puts the watch down, chuckling at it.* HE *stops short. Then, like harsh commands:*

Back! Back, back, back, back!

HE *runs his fingers down the page until he reaches "Noonan."*

Noonan, Noonan, Noonan, Noonan, Noonan, Noonan, Noonan, Noonan, Noonan . . . Noonan, *No*onan, Mary C. There. Keep at it. Hmmmm.

HE *stares at the audience.*

Mary Noonan. Mary C. Noonan.

HE *stares, silently.*

. . . Clairrrr.

HE *rolls his eyes up at the ceiling and sighs.*

Mary Claire Noonan. Mary . . .

HE *pauses. Then, slowly, instead of "Claire":*

Jane.

HE *slowly lowers his eyes to the audience.*

Ma-ry *Jane.*

HE *prolongs the vowel sound of "Jane" and looks intensely at the audience. Gradually his expression changes to one of sorrow, then despair.* HE *blinks his eyes. Tears roll down his cheeks.* HE *slowly turns to one side, stares at the empty space, puts out his hand and strokes the head of an imaginary girl, making small catlike sounds.* HE *stops abruptly, stares at several points behind him quickly, as if frightened, then stumbles to his bed and rummages beneath it.* HE *throws eight or nine telephone books behind him, and miscellaneous other matter, finds what he wants —a short piece of rope—and returns to the table.* HE *sits and fumbles furiously making a noose, slips it over his head, holds the end high over his head, and stares without expression at the audience, head tilted. Gradually his eyes open wide and bulge,* HE *gurgles and chokes, his face turns white and purple. Static, then heart-warming music.* HE *drops the rope and pounds the radio angrily. Static, then dead.* HE *waits. Nothing.* HE *picks up his watch, looks at it, and lets out a long moan. Then* HE *stops short, looks at his watch again.*

Six fifty-nine? Six fifty-nine?

HE *hits the radio furiously. Static, then a voice.*

RADIO When you hear the gong it will be exactly seven thirty-one and *(Pause)* seventeen seconds.

There is no gong. HE *waits, looks up at the audience. After half a minute, a gong.*

MAN Hah! *(*HE *grits his teeth)* Hah! *(*HE *sucks his breath)* Hah!

Again HE *looks at the audience for a minute, then looks at the telephone book, places his hand heavily on it, and slides it a little nearer. In a rather tired voice:*

Noonan, Noonan, Noonan, Noonan, Gregory. No. Noonan, John. No. Noonan, Joseph. No. Noonan . . .

HE *pauses a long time. Then, slowly.*

Ma-ry.

HE *stares again at the audience. Time passes. Suddenly, with lightning speed,* HE *leaps up, raises the radio above his head, and smashes it on the floor, stamping on it furiously while* HE *grunts from the exertion.* HE *stops, panting, picks up his chair, sits. Slowly,* HE *takes his watch and looks at it. Then* HE *raises his eyes to the audience. In a monotone:*

When you hear the gong, it will be exactly seven thirty-one and *(Pause)* seventeen seconds. When you hear the gong, it will be exactly seven thirty-one and *(Pause)* seventeen seconds. When you hear the gong, it will be exactly seven thirty-one and *(Pause)* seventeen seconds.

The lights dim.

When you hear the gong, it will be exactly seven thirty-one and *(Pause)* seventeen seconds. When you hear the gong, it will be exactly seven thirty-one and *(Pause)* seventeen seconds.

Pitch black.

When you hear the gong, it will be exactly seven thirty-one and *(Pause)* seventeen seconds. When you hear the gong, it will be exactly seven thirty-one and *(Pause)* seventeen seconds.

Silence. One gong.

THE LOVERS

" . . . in lust they burn . . ."

Paradise Lost, Book IX

"They, looking back, all the eastern side beheld

Of Paradise, so late their happy seat . . ."

Paradise Lost, Book XII

The Lovers was first performed in the Playwrights Workshop of the Actors Studio on January 16, 1967. It was directed by Douglas Taylor, with the following cast:

Adam *Jeff Tambornino*
Evie *Judi West*

The play was subsequently performed, in a slightly revised version, by the New Theatre Workshop on a series of Monday nights beginning February 17, 1969. This production was directed by John Vaccaro, with the following cast:

Adam *Jack Aaron*
Evie *Crystal Field*

THE LOVERS

CHARACTERS: ADAM, EVIE. Both are in their mid-twenties. Neither is very attractive, but this is in part the result of dress and attitude rather than poor features.

A darkened room. A disembodied VOICE *recites the two quotations from Milton. A rusty alarm clock rings.* ADAM *moans.* HE *wakes up slowly, sits on his bed, rubbing himself, then stands and pulls a string attached to a light.* HE *blinks in surprise, then smiles awkwardly and rubs himself again, as if to make sure he is all there.* HE *looks around the room in wonder. It is a nondescript clutter of odds and ends, "found" junk. On all the available wall space are blown-up pinup pictures, some nude, some pornographic, most of them selling a product. For example, a girl's crotch may feature a bunch of broccoli with the lettering "Eat broccoli for good health." To one side is a table on which there are a box, a pot of paste, magazines, scissors, a bowl of rotten fruit, and several racks from which hang various pieces of hair, fur, string, and strips of colored paper, mostly in crescent and moon shapes. To one side of the table is a life-size, female store dummy. It is nude, wigless, and dead. On the other side of the table there is a small portable record machine. In the rear are a pile of junk, a bed, and a refrigerator.* ADAM *shuffles stiffly to the window, yawning, pulls up the shade, which breaks, and opens the window, which faces a faded brick wall. Dirt blows in.* HE *coughs.*

ADAM *(Shutting the window and brushing himself)* Oi vey.

HE *shuffles, less stiffly now, to the table, sits, and eats a shriveled banana as* HE *gazes vacantly into space around him, finally focusing on one of the pictures. It gives him an idea, and* HE *suddenly throws the peel away and begins examining his magazines eagerly. Selecting a* Life, HE *flicks the pages with determination, stopping at intervals to rip out pages, from some of which* HE *cuts out more shapes like those on the racks.* HE *hums with pleasant absorption—the busy bee at his work—as he does this. Finally*

HE *cuts out a vermilion crescent that especially pleases him and gives several grunts and giggles of approval.* HE *stands up and kisses his fingers to the air.*

Magnifique!

HE *dances around the room ecstatically, holding the crescent aloft.*

Ummph! *Magnifique! Magnifique!*

HE *interrupts his reverie to rush to the phonograph and put on a record. It is a waltz. With grace and excitement, more or less rhythmically,* HE *rushes back and forth from the dummy to the table. Using the pot of paste,* HE *places his bit of paper between her legs, steps back, looks at her, takes the paper off and trims it knowledgeably, then puts it back.* HE *adds, with similar care, a wig, pubic hair or fur, and pasties. Then* HE *crayons the eyes and mouth. His excitement mounts and* HE *begins to laugh a little idiotically to himself. In the end,* HE *stands back, slightly bent, with clenched hands, grinning, grunting, and laughing at his work. An idea strikes him.* HE *rips off the pasties, rummages frantically through the box on the table and comes up with two baby bottle nipples. These* HE *jabs into the jar of paste and sticks on the dummy's breasts. The result surpasses his wildest dreams.* HE *leaps through the air to the phonograph and drops the next record. It is a wild, rhythmic piece, to which* HE *does a sensual but essentially awkward and funny dance before the dummy. As* HE *dances,* EVIE *comes in and stands by the door looking at him, half-fascinated, half-repelled. At the climactic moments of the dance, just after* HE *has grasped and pulled off one of the nipples with his teeth,* SHE *walks across the room, turns off the music, and assumes a pose of dummy-like sexuality.* ADAM*'s dance disintegrates in confusion.* HE *turns around, the nipple still in his mouth, sounds of outrage gurgling in his throat.*

Why the hell don't you knock? Can't a guy have privacy anymore?

EVIE *(Breaking her pose)* I live here, you degenerate.

ADAM A guy's got to relax, Evie!

EVIE *(Hysterically, turning on him)* And I want a baby. I want a baby! *I want a baby!*

ADAM *sits down wearily and sticks the nipple on the box.*

ADAM *(In a mildly scolding manner)* You gonna start with that again?

EVIE *(Screaming) Make me a baby, you stinking crud!!!*

ADAM *(Holding up his hands to pacify)* All right, all right. So don't get in a sweat over it.

HE *is about to say more, but sees* SHE *is about to burst if he does.* THEY *remain silent a few seconds,* SHE *staring at him,* HE *fingering the objects on his rack.*

Jesus, *your old man!* I mean, just because your old man wants to be a grandfather, *I* have to suffer. What does he think I am, one of his goddamned rabbits?

EVIE You ain't even a sloth. With fungus all over him even a sloth reproduces.

ADAM *(Laughing a little stupidly at his wit)* You find me that fungus and I'll reproduce.

EVIE *(Bitterly)* Oh, I'd like to fungus you, all right! Right through the floor!

HE *laughs at her frustration, then stops abruptly as a thought strikes him.*

ADAM Hey, did you know I get nightmares about your old man? *Yeah.* He comes after me with this big fuckin beard and—

EVIE Don't you dare talk about him in that tone of voice!

ADAM What? Dare? What tone of voice?

EVIE Disrespectful, that's what.

ADAM Well, he's a goddamned bully. He scares the living shit out of me.

EVIE *(Bitterly)* You owe him everything.

ADAM *(Sweeping his arm to include the room)* Yeah. Yeah. You're right. I'm not grateful enough. *(HE is silent a few seconds, to let his gesture sink in)* Look at it. A dump. Why did we have to move? Huh? We had a nice place where we was. Elevator, hot water, plenty of light, no cockroaches. But you, *you had to move!! You* had to put a bug up my ass. The Bronx wasn't good enough for you. No, not you.

EVIE So I made a mistake. So what? You never made a mistake? I'm only human, you know.

ADAM I know, I know. Human. So look where it got us—Brooklyn! *(With utter despair) Brooklyn!* . . . Central Park South, you said. Beautiful swans we'd watch, gliding in the pond. Manhattan! Where the action was! The beautiful people! Fucking on the terrace with a view!—Evie, your old man is a cheapskate.

EVIE *(Pointing her finger at him)* You! You ought to be ashamed of yourself, Adam. Two long years we been married and already you are a degenerate. That's what you are, a degenerate.

ADAM *(Cackling)* Hah! So in Brooklyn what do you expect?

EVIE We're married people, and married people are supposed to have kids. *(SHE pauses a few moments, then, yelling)* We're supposed to *multiply!!*

ADAM With you I should multiply?

EVIE What's wrong with me? I'm a girl, no? I got plenty on the ball. I am a swinger. I got a good shape. *(SHE takes a few rapid steps toward him, stands on a chair, and raises her skirt) A good shape, Adam!!*

ADAM Evie, I ain't eaten.

EVIE Degenerate!

ADAM So I'm *sorry.* Evie, you just don't send me anymore. Maybe it's the air's polluted. *You don't send me.*

EVIE *(Dropping her skirt and getting off the chair)* And in the Bronx I did?

ADAM It was different.

EVIE Whadaya mean, different?

ADAM *(At a loss)* I dunno. We had Van Cortlandt Park . . . and the zoo—Evie, I even used to go bird watching. *Me.*

EVIE So what's wrong with Prospect Park? It's got grass. I seen plenty of birds there.

ADAM Ugh! Filthy pigeons crapping all over, that's Prospect Park. Don't talk about it. Even the fish are sick. —Oh, Evie, it was just easier. It, it wasn't so hard. I mean—it didn't seem like . . . like so much . . . work. *(Tenderly)* You know?

EVIE Hah. Work, he says. *I* do all the work!

ADAM (*Petulantly*) I don't want to talk about it.

EVIE You couldn't even take a pill?

ADAM What kind of pill?

EVIE How should I know? A pep pill. Serutan. One-a-day vitamins. *Anything.* Ask in the drugstore. You never heard what them Italian movie actors do?

ADAM (*Bored*) What?

EVIE Dope. (*Pointing to her buttocks*) They stick it in with a needle.

ADAM And what happens?

EVIE (*Laughing to herself*) What happens? Like firecrackers, that's what happens. All night. It should happen to you. Ha ha, I made a funny.

ADAM You know, you're getting morbid. You shouldn't breathe so much.

EVIE (*A deliberate insult*) *You Brooklyn bum.*

SHE *goes to the phonograph, puts on a record, and, after a few seconds, dances a wild and funny fertility dance in front of him, shaking, bumping, grinding, lifting her skirt.* ADAM *resolutely cuts shapes from a magazine until* SHE *slaps the scissors from his hands.* HE *walks to the phonograph and turns it off.* EVIE *stands still, watching him.* HE *picks up the scissors, returns to the table, and resumes cutting.*

ADAM (*Dispassionately*) You're disgusting.

EVIE *flops into an adjacent chair.*

You hear me? You're disgusting.

EVIE Sure. Sure, I hear you. And you over there with the valentines, you're the spitting image of an angel, I suppose? Hah!

ADAM *(Amused)* Hah!

EVIE Boy. How did I ever get hooked up with you? You are the Leonardi da Vinci of degenerates. For you a whole Greenwich Village wouldn't be enough.

ADAM I love you, too.

SHE *studies him as* HE *works. Suddenly:*

EVIE Why don't you ever use a higher type magazine?

ADAM *(Interested, and pleased that the conversation has taken a different turn)* Such as?

EVIE Oh, I don't know. *The Atlantic Monthly. The Saturday Review. Publications of the Modern Language Association.*

ADAM Stupid. No color, that's why. Cheesy magazines. They don't do me nothing.

EVIE It's got to have color?

ADAM *(Looking at her cautiously, unsure of her sincerity)* Nooo. *(*HE *pauses. Then, a little excited)* Once I colored her all black, and then I used only white. Typing paper. Bond. Damned good stuff.

EVIE *(Impressed)* Jesus! What was it like?

SHE *drapes a leg over him, and, as the scene continues, works her way into an embrace of sorts.*

ADAM *(Swallowing a grin)* Pretty damn good. *(With emphasis) Pretty damn good. (*HE *makes a strong snip with the scissors)* All black with a white—

EVIE Christ!

ADAM *(Slobbering) Yeah. (*HE *waves his hand downward; his tongue hangs out)*

EVIE You ever tried *chartreuse?*

ADAM What's that?

EVIE Sorta like a parakeet color. *(Cutely, with fluttering and wiggling gestures)* You know, like them little birdies in the five and dime?

ADAM *(Laughing a little stupidly)* No. —But I got a few feathers. *(Biting his lip) Crazy!*

EVIE How about spaghetti orange? You go for that?

ADAM *(Excited, holding up an orange crescent)* Like this? You mean like this?

EVIE Yeah, that's it. *(Coyly)* But with lots more sauce.

ADAM *(Proudly)* Campbell's tomato soup.

EVIE Makes your mouth water, huh? A real breakthrough in cosmetics.

ADAM *(Surprised at her perception)* Yeah. Yeah. Most of them soups are good. That's why I get *Good Housekeeping* and *The Ladies Home Journal* and—and *McCalls.* I had a *great* cream of mushroom once! *(*HE *is practically jumping out of his seat)* And the *National Geographic*—oi, oi! Them African tangerines!

EVIE *(Sensing that* HE *is too far out)* Hey, what's that big lumpy one over there, like a wrinkled turnip?

ADAM *(Pointing)* This one?

EVIE Yeah.

ADAM *(Sheepishly)* That's for Halloween.

EVIE *(Giggling)* Hey, that's cute.

ADAM *(Touched)* You really think so, Evie? I . . . I . . . *(HE cannot find words)*

EVIE *(Softly, but nevertheless urgently)* Adam?

ADAM What?

EVIE You know, I'd do anything for you, Adam.

ADAM You would? Would you, Evie?

EVIE What's your favorite soup or vegetable? Tell me. Go on, tell me. Any color at all. *(Coaxing)* Tell me.

ADAM *(Like a small explosion)* Birdseye broccoli! —Oh! *(The words do something to him. HE jumps up excitedly, holding his crotch and stumping around. HE makes several jerky movements, lets out some smothered whoops, and heads for the phonograph)*

EVIE *(In despair)* Adam!

ADAM *(Turning, the arm of the phonograph in his hand)* What? For Christ's sake, what?

EVIE Why isn't it the same for us in Brooklyn? Why? *Why?*

ADAM Ask your old man!

EVIE Adam! *Tell me why!*

ADAM *(Indecisive, then determined)* Because—because you *fart* in Brooklyn!

HE *drops the needle and begins to dance wildly, putting a green crescent over the previous one and adding a large hat and a red navel to the dummy's decor.* EVIE *watches for a few moments in complete defeat. Then, defiantly,* SHE *runs to the rear of the room and drags out another dummy, more decrepit, obviously one of* ADAM*'s discards.* SHE *stands it up and begins dancing with determination.* THEY *dance competitively,* EVIE *putting pubic hair on the dummy's head, chin, and chest.* SHE *stops twice more, once to get two large blue bulbs, which* SHE *hangs in front of the dummy, and once to get a long salami from the refrigerator to hang between the bulbs.* SHE *then becomes as caught up in the frenzy as* ADAM. THEY *gradually drop, quivering in ecstasy, to the floor and grope painfully towards one another, embracing, in a frantic clutch, as the lights dim to* EVIE*'s fervent, "Oh, Daddy, Daddy, Daddy, Daddy!"*

Over: Ellen Stewart introduces
the La Mama production
of *The Monkeys of the Organ Grinder*

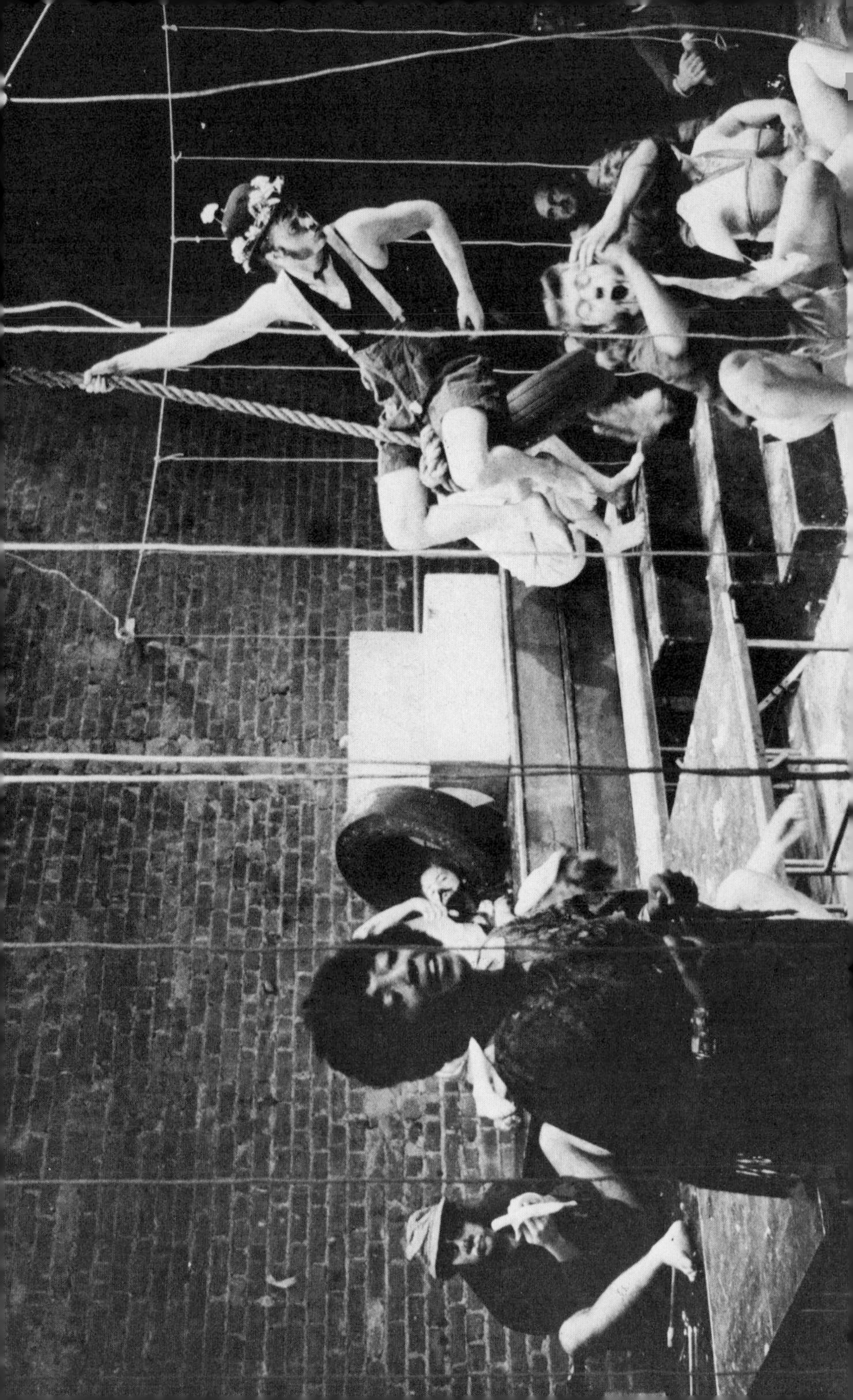

THE MONKEYS OF THE ORGAN GRINDER

The Monkeys of the Organ Grinder was first performed at the New Theatre Workshop on February 17, 1969. It was directed by John Vaccaro, with the following cast:

Betsy *Crystal Field*
Freddie *William Ostroff*
Regina *Frank Dudley*
Bernstein *Jack Aaron*
Lucius *Danny Goldman*
Algernon *Rob Kilgallen*
Photographer *John Blakeney*

It was subsequently performed by the Wherehouse-La MaMa London Troupe, in their American debut, at Brecht West in New Brunswick, New Jersey, and at La Mama E.T.C. in New York, September 24–30, 1970. This production was also directed by John Vaccaro, with lighting by John P. Dodd, and the following cast:

Betsy *Beth Porter*
Freddie *Peter Reid*
Regina *Joyce Stanton*
Bernstein *Paddy Swanson*
Lucius *David Bonnar*
Photographer *Kevin Bradigan*
Algernon *Otto Erotica*

CHARACTERS

REGINA, a bearded lady
FREDDIE, a picture slasher
BETSY, a prostitute
BERNSTEIN, an organ grinder
LUCIUS, a hunchback
ALGERNON, a policeman
PHOTOGRAPHER

SCENE: *A room. It is cluttered with drab furniture, including a table, several chairs, a bed, and a bureau with a mirror. There are no windows.* REGINA *is sleeping in the bed. On the wall there are several large indistinguishable paintings, mostly in ornate frames.* FREDDIE *stands in a corner as if hiding or waiting.* HE *steps out, strolls around the room casually, even a little jauntily, then quickly and gracefully flicks open a knife, slashes a painting, puts the knife away, and walks off, whistling.* HE *tries several such maneuvers, during which* BETSY, *young, shapely, in brilliant red panties and bra, walks in.* SHE *watches him a minute silently.*

BETSY *(Cheerfully)* Hi, Freddie. How's tricks?

HE *puts up a silencing hand, meditates a few seconds, then deftly performs a complicated maneuver whereby an entire painting hangs out of the frame.* HE *gives her a quick look of triumph, then takes down the painting and puts another one up.* HE *sits at the table and nods to her to come over.* SHE *does.*

FREDDIE *(Conspiratorially)* Last Tuesday. In the A.M. Gallery 32 in the Corcoran. Wearing my Brooks Brothers. Guy in a boat. Soldier. Ice in water. White hair, red nose.

BETSY What color's his eyes?

FREDDIE White.

BETSY I think I know the guy.

FREDDIE Dead.

BETSY It figures.

FREDDIE Waltzed right up. *(With appropriate slashing motions)* Psst, psst, psst! Three times. Fast. Gillette. All drowned. Out like a bird.

BETSY Gosh, that's wonderful, Freddie. I don't know how you do it.

FREDDIE *(Pinching her nipple and winking)* Practice. I practice. All the time.

BETSY *(Rubbing her nipple)* Gee, I sure got to hand it to you, Freddie.

FREDDIE It's nothing.

BETSY It's more than nothing.

FREDDIE Okay. It's more than nothing.

THEY *look at one another and laugh with the understanding of the initiated.*

REGINA *(Sitting up with a loud yawn)* Great holy Christ in the morning! What time is it?

REGINA *is a tall woman with a long, straight beard. Her body, wherever her nightgown reveals it, is hairy, especially her chest, which* SHE *rubs.* SHE *speaks more or less oracularly.*

BETSY Hi, doll.

REGINA Kiss me, Freddie, you virgin's dream.

FREDDIE Psst!

BETSY Oh, you kids.

FREDDIE *(Laughing a little stupidly)* Fuckin drowned.

REGINA *(Getting out of bed abruptly, yawning and stretching)* I'm hungry, *hungry,* HUNGRY.

BETSY You mind if I take five? It's the full moon and my ass aches like hell.

REGINA Nope. Sack out, you minion of Aphrodite.

BETSY *(Crawling into the bed and mumbling)* Six Armenians, one Turk, and a delegation from Carpathia. A monk with sixteen prayers and a whammy. One nearsighted Russian with a nit scab. Sheep herder from Montana with size five sweater. Baaa. Trombone player with trombone. Two society women and one society plumber. Elk local. Half a Siamese twin. Man with eighty teeth from Winnipeg. Great Dane. Man named Llewellyn. Valedictorian from St. Julius High—

A loud buzzer sounds. SHE *leaps up.*

Oh, shit, I'll see you later, kids.

SHE *leaves, clutching her buttocks.*

REGINA I'm hungry, husband. Love famishes me.

FREDDIE Psst, psst, psst! Fuckin drowned.

HE *puts a ripped painting on the table and begins taping it.* REGINA *does sitting-up exercises.*

REGINA You sure know how to lay it into a girl, Freddie. You lovely beast!

FREDDIE *(Conspiratorially)* New York. Two weeks ago Friday. The Frick. Nude girl. Hard up. Looking at an apple. Rich. No tits. Psst, psst, psst! Three times up the ass. Out like a bird.

REGINA You're too ambitious, honeybumpkin. Listen, you don't have to be a kingpin for me. I don't need no wheeler and dealer if I have my nights of love.

THEY *laugh.* FREDDIE *continues his work. Sound of street music from an organ.* BERNSTEIN *and* LUCIUS *enter.* BERNSTEIN *is fat and middle-aged.* LUCIUS *is a hunchback of indeterminate age.* HE *dances to* BERNSTEIN*'s organ music as* HE *enters, until it stops abruptly, whereupon* HE *loses his balance slightly.*

BERNSTEIN Stop, stop, my pet. Let us rest our weary passions in this haven of love.

LUCIUS *looks at* BERNSTEIN *a moment, then rushes to* REGINA *and rubs up against her clumsily and lasciviously.*

REGINA *(Peeling him off)* Easy, my sweet. My favors are not so easily bought.

LUCIUS *retires to a corner and eats fruit greedily.*

FREDDIE Three weeks ago Sunday. Baltimore. Girl with—

BERNSTEIN *(Interrupting)* He's a playful lad, Lucius. But I promised his mother. And true I shall be to that dear dead woman, how she suffered.

REGINA *(Now lifting weights)* Heigh-ho, he is. And I'll bet my bottom to that. Hah!

FREDDIE *(Looking menacingly at* BERNSTEIN*)* Psst, psst, psst!

REGINA *(Looking at* FREDDIE *like a sick cow)* I'm famished. Love gives me a very special appetite.

FREDDIE *laughs stupidly.*

BERNSTEIN You're just a couple of kittens. But . . . is the urinary tract functioning? The liver? The pineal gland? Does he rest?

BETSY *(Kicking the door open as* BERNSTEIN *stops speaking)* I need the rest, you better believe it. *(*SHE *goes to the bed, clutching her buttocks, and rolls into the blanket)*

LUCIUS *(Suddenly aroused)* Yeah! You just take the Arafura Sea. The-the-the Arafura Sea. In the deep water, sharks. Big sharks. In the shallow water, poisonous yellow sea snakes. Millions. Then mud flats. Slimy. Miles of them. Swarming with crocodiles. And, and, and then mangroves. Thicker than nerves or—or pubic hair. And then the jungle, and snakes, and savages. Jesus! Who the hell do you think you are, anyway? You—you just try to get through! You just try!

BERNSTEIN *(Thumbing a worn pocket notebook)* One thousand, nine hundred . . . *(Closing his eyes)* I hear a waltz. *(A brief, bitter laugh)*

LUCIUS And—and the mice in *Yugoslavia.* In the *Balkans.* Two hundred miles of corn, rye, wheat, bean, and potatoes. Eaten. Eaten up. All of it. In one month. F-f-f-from Sarajevo to Priboj. Millions of mice teeth. Jesus! You just try it! Try it! Boy!

BERNSTEIN *puts away his notebook and cranks the organ.*

BETSY *(Sitting up)* Hey, knock it off, kike. There's a lady in the house.

BERNSTEIN *(With a bow)* A thousand pardons! I thought maybe the music . . . We are . . . A thousand pardons! *(*HE *sinks into thought)*

LUCIUS And the Ethiopian crocodile. *Twenty feet long even!* They *smash* canoes like toothpicks on the Omo River. *Omoooooo!* They *eat* the *people*. They *eat* the *bones!* They *crack* them! You just try it! Yeah! Boy! *(*HE *scratches his crotch, then eats more fruit greedily)* Lousy Jew slave driver. Yid bastard. *Moslem!* Boy. Pennies. He gives me pennies.

BERNSTEIN *goes to him abruptly and beats him to the floor.*

Ow! Ow! *(Growling and trying to bite* BERNSTEIN*'s shoes)* My hump! It's breaking! Master-r-r-r-r!

REGINA Bernie, Bernie, Bernie. You'll break the boy's *spirit.*

BERNSTEIN *(Panting)* You're right. *(Kicking* LUCIUS*)* He's a thoroughbred. *(Kicking him again)* He's a highly strung organism. *(*HE *stops abruptly, takes out his notebook and writes. Then, abstracted,* HE *looks up and waves a finger in time to some interior music. Smiling)* Apples . . . golden apples . . .

LUCIUS *(Muttering as he half-raises himself)* You just try it! Boy! Piranha! King cobras! Baboons! Christ! They kill *leopards!*

FREDDIE *(Jabbing* BERNSTEIN*)* Psst! Five weeks ago yesterday. Cleveland. Main floor, rear. Guy in castle. Fur collar. Big nose, needs a haircut. Wearing a cock bag. *I* was wearing my truss. *(With a long, clean movement)* Psssssst! Got me a pair of balls. Out like a bird.

BETSY Gee. What a guy.

BERNSTEIN Remarkable.

REGINA He knows how to lay it into a gal, I can tell you. Jumping Jehoshaphat!

LUCIUS *(Standing up)* You just try it! Scorpions! Mad gorillas! *Lockjaw!*

BERNSTEIN Music is called for. It's quite clear. We must drown out the silence with measure and melody.

HE *plays his organ.* LUCIUS *and* REGINA *dance. The door bursts open and* ALGERNON *walks in.* HE *is in uniform. Everyone is still.* HE *walks around suspiciously, picking off* BETSY*'s blanket with his night stick, looking inside her pants, tapping* BERNSTEIN*'s organ, staring at* LUCIUS, *etc. Then, quickly,* HE *whips off his jacket, shirt and undershirt, puts on a brassiere, sprawls on a chair, and puts two oranges in the bra.*

ALGERNON I'm here on official business.

BERNSTEIN You got a badge?

LUCIUS You just try it. Like a pit full of yellow spiders! Bloodsuckers! Pig killers! Eye-gougers!

ALGERNON I have a Roman numeral. I am on the vice squad.

The loud buzzer sounds again.

BETSY Shit. Now I'll never know. (SHE *walks out holding her buttocks, returns almost immediately and bends over double, her buttocks near* ALGERNON*'s face)* You wouldn't believe how quick some guys can make it. Shoot.

ALGERNON *(Staring at her)* A serious crime has been committed. I have come to interrogate.

BETSY I don't think I can cope.

ALGERNON What?

BETSY *Cope!*

ALGERNON Not on duty. Where were you the night of August 14 at four-thirty A.M.?

BETSY I was spread out.

ALGERNON You admit it?

BETSY What year?

ALGERNON The present.

BETSY Forget it, buster. I have a mattress stuffed with pricks.

ALGERNON Next!

BETSY *returns to the bed.* REGINA *walks up and takes the same position.* ALGERNON *stares a long time, then reaches under her nightgown and pulls out a dead rabbit, which* HE *tosses on the table.* HE *gets up, fluffs his breasts as* REGINA *falls into a sitting position in the chair.*

Aha! Aha!— Have you anything to say?

REGINA I'm exhausted. —From the time I was eight I have shaved at least once a day.

ALGERNON Any more?

REGINA I've had three growths of teeth.

ALGERNON Aha!

REGINA My heart—

ALGERNON Yes?

REGINA My heart—

ALGERNON Yes?

REGINA My heart—

ALGERNON *Yes?*

REGINA —is on my left side.

ALGERNON And?

REGINA I've had dating problems.

ALGERNON *(Angrily)* I won't have you lying! I'll have no disrespect for the law!

FREDDIE Psst, psst, psst!

ALGERNON *(Rushing up to him)* Yes? Yes? Can you help me? Please. Help me. I'll give you a fortune. Wealth, I mean.

FREDDIE *(Conspiratorially)* Fourteen weeks ago last Wednesday. The Fine Arts in Boston. Jewish holiday. Wearing a black vest from Abercrombie and Fitch.

ALGERNON *(Excited)* Go on, man! Go on!

FREDDIE *(Holding up his hand and winking)* Girl milking a cow. Labor Day weekend.

ALGERNON Don't stop! Give me everything!

FREDDIE Blonde. Fat ass.

ALGERNON Yes? Yes?

FREDDIE Wearing my sneaks. White rose. Very chic.

ALGERNON And? What then, man?

FREDDIE *(Getting down to it)* Well, she was bent over, see? Nice boobs. Cow giving her the eye.

ALGERNON Finish! You're almost there!

FREDDIE Old geezer peeking round the corner of the barn. Competition. Don't like. Psst, psst, psst! Cut him out of the picture. Out like a bird.

ALGERNON *(Laughing a little hysterically)* That's it! That's it! Don't you see, you blind fools? There wasn't any man in the picture. He was *outside* the picture.

As HE *continues to laugh,* BERNSTEIN *plays his organ and* LUCIUS *advances on him.*

And that man was—

LUCIUS *sticks a knife in one of* ALGERNON*'s breasts. The music stops. Everyone is silent as* ALGERNON *looks at the knife, stunned. Then* HE *realizes that it is not his real breast and begins to laugh uncontrollably.* HE *pulls the knife out; his breast overflows with blood.* HE *shrieks, then collapses, dead.*

BETSY Boy. What a life. I'm telling you.

BERNSTEIN Disastrous.

LUCIUS You just try it! Quicksand! Rats in the sewers! Foo Manchoo!

BERNSTEIN *(Writing in his notebook)* A consummation devoutly to be achieved.

BETSY *(Massaging her buttocks)* Don't remind me.

A knock at the door. THEY *are silent a few moments.*

BERNSTEIN It's he.

BETSY So soon?

REGINA But I haven't even trimmed.

FREDDIE Trim your ass. *(*HE *laughs stupidly)*

REGINA *(A blushing bride)* Bosh.

LUCIUS *(Subdued)* Well, you just try it, anyway. Barracuda. Gangrene. The Yellow Menace.

BERNSTEIN Let him in, my dear. It's . . . about time.

BETSY *walks prettily to the door, flings it open, and dances ballet steps backwards to* BERNSTEIN*'s music. A young, serious, very properly dressed* PHOTOGRAPHER *walks in with a tripod camera.* HE *speaks humbly and somewhat nervously.*

PHOTOGRAPHER I'm . . . I'm from Ace. Are you . . . the folks?

ALL *(Eagerly)* Yes. Yes. Yes.

PHOTOGRAPHER *(Reading from a brochure, each statement an end in itself)* I am from Ace. I am twenty-four years of age and in perfect health. I am a college graduate.

As HE *reads,* THEY *become more impressed and happy.*

I have all my teeth and sleep eight hours a night. My penis is three inches in repose and six erectile. My tongue is never coated. I served Freedom's cause for two years and received an honorable discharge. I eschew vulgarity. I say my prayers regularly. I love my mother. *(HE looks up shyly)* Sufficient?

REGINA Delighted, I'm sure. I myself was born of a congenital imbecile. Freddie?

FREDDIE Last Sunday. In the P.M. The Modern Art. Guy in a sailboat.

BERNSTEIN You'd like us grouped, of course?

PHOTOGRAPHER Well . . . yes. I . . . I think that would be . . . nice.

LUCIUS *(Excited again)* You just try it! Millions of cockroaches in the reservoir! Germs in the meat!

BERNSTEIN *touches his shoulder gently. Subdued, eager to please:*

Here? Here all right?

HE *notices the* PHOTOGRAPHER *looking at* ALGERNON'S *body. Laughing.*

Oh, him.

PHOTOGRAPHER Er, not at all. Not at all. I mean—Well, you did say a group picture. *(HE smiles faintly)* It's for the record, you know. The *permanent* record.

BETSY *(Snapping her pants)* By God, he did. Come on, everybody. A little life! *Life!*

REGINA Freddie?

FREDDIE Psst, psst, psst!

THEY *group just behind* ALGERNON*'s body, and the* PHOTOGRAPHER *sets up his tripod.* HE *seems about to take the picture several times, but stops, shrugs, and smiles faintly, after which* THEY *regroup, each time more intimately and affectionately, using the sofa. In the final tableau,* BERNSTEIN *sits with a stiff grin.* BETSY *lies across the sofa with her head and shoulders in his lap.* SHE *holds up* ALGERNON*'s head from the floor and cuddles it.* REGINA *sits on the floor beside* BERNSTEIN, *her legs spread, and* LUCIUS *sits inside her legs, his body inside her nightgown, his head sticking out of her chest, his tongue happily out.* FREDDIE *lies across the back of the sofa, his head on the other side of* BERNSTEIN. THEY *seem at last to have the perfect tableau and wait stiffly and impatiently.*

PHOTOGRAPHER That's fine, folks. Just fine. It's really an Ace portrait. Now, now, you all just hold it, just hold it right there. Okay, now everybody say "fly."

Their faces all form a silent "fly." HE *pushes a button. A spray of lather squirts out of the camera for half a minute, onto their faces and bodies.* THEY *remain frozen. The* PHOTOGRAPHER *straightens up, stares at them, and breaks into a demonic, high-pitched laughter which quickly becomes hysterical. As the lights go out, street organ music.*

THE GIANTS IN THE EARTH

CHARACTERS

HARRY
JAKE
PERLMUTTER
THREE MORE SOLDIERS
RADIO VOICES

SCENE: *A small, dimly lit subterranean military post in the Antarctic. Outside, above, are wind and ice, subzero temperatures, and vast empty spaces. Around the perimeter of the installation, thick ice is visible, so that the total effect is that of a small burrow of civilization in a world of hostile wind and ice. A triple bunk takes up most of one wall, footlockers on either side of it and one under the bottom bunk. The opposite wall is covered with equipment: radio, radar, weather instruments. On the wall connecting these two there is a door leading to a small toilet. On one side of the door, more equipment, heavy clothing, rifles; a ladder leading outside. The equipment is big, shiny, and impressive. The whole enclosure is, in a sense, one large complex piece of equipment; it bristles with technological achievement. During the play, some of the equipment can be seen fluctuating. On the other side of the door, a small stove with cabinet for dishes, pots, etc. In the middle of the room, a table and chairs over a trap door leading to a pit for storage and power equipment. All available cups, saucers, pots, and pans are out, scattered all over the room in every conceivable resting place. Throughout the play the room changes dimensions, becoming smaller until Scene 4, when it becomes larger. In Scene 5 it is quite small. Sound of clogged toilet, which through the play steadily becomes more insistent.*

SCENE 1

Strange radio-like echoes. Sound of cracking ice. The room shudders. Sound of helicopter. Then muffled sounds, as of people stomping above. Dimly seen figures. The hatch on top opens. Voices, speaking over the wind.

HARRY Whatya think, Sarge?

JAKE I dunno. *Hello below! Hello below! This is your relief party! Are you there?*

HARRY They don't answer.

JAKE I'm going in. Cover me.

HARRY Right.

Rifle clicks.

JAKE *Hello! Hello! We're coming in! Repeat: we're coming in! (Silence)* Cover me.

HARRY Right.

JAKE *scrambles down the ladder quickly, stumbles and falls over.* HE *rises quickly, swings out his carbine, and stands alert for trouble. After a few moments* HE *finds and switches on the lights. Sound of clogged toilet.* HE *tenses, advances slowly to the toilet door, kicks it open, and rushes in. Silence, then the sound of urine in the toilet.*

Hey, Sarge! We're freezing our balls off up here!

Continued sound of urine in the toilet.

Have a heart!

The toilet flushes loudly.

JAKE *(Coming out of the toilet, adjusting his clothes)* Yeah? What balls, baby?

HARRY C'mon, Sarge! How about it?

JAKE *looks around at the disarray with a puzzled expression.* HE *turns around quickly several times, as if sensing someone behind him.* HE *walks to different parts of the installation, pauses, rubs his finger for dust, looks around him.* HE *seems to be thinking.*

Hey! Sarge! Jake! *C'mon!*

JAKE Yeah. Okay. *Come on down.*

PERLMUTTER What did he say?

HARRY We're going in.

Several large sacks are thrown down. They are followed by HARRY *and* PERLMUTTER, *heavily dressed and with carbines.* THEY *begin shucking their outer clothes and rubbing and blowing their hands.*

Jeez. Do I gotta piss. *(*HE *does)*

JAKE Perlmutter!

PERLMUTTER *(Jumping)* Huh?

JAKE Shut the fuckin hatch.

PERLMUTTER *climbs up, shuts the hatch, and returns.*

HARRY *(With a brief, gleeful laugh, clapping his hands as* HE *leaves the toilet)* Well, we made it, Sarge. We made it.

JAKE *(Looking around slowly)* Yeah. We made it. Home sweet home.

PERLMUTTER Yeah. *(*HE *almost sits on the lower bunk, sees the crockery, and jumps up)* Hey, for . . .

HARRY Boy. Six lousy fuckin months. *(Clowning)* And no goils. *(HE laughs)*

PERLMUTTER Good riddance, I say. They only take you for a ride.

HARRY That's because you scare them with that Jewish cock of yours, Perlmutter. These girls don't know from kosher. They're pure blood American.

PERLMUTTER Yeah? Indians, I suppose, huh?

HARRY Yeah. . . . Want to make something of it?

JAKE *(A little too vehemently)* Shut up!

An uneasy silence. Sound of clogged toilet.

HARRY Gee, take it easy, Jake. *(Silence. With suppressed excitement)* Hey. What do you think happened, Jake? Huh? You got any idea?

JAKE *(Irritably)* Look at this goddam place. Filthy. Like pigs lived here. Didn't nobody ever do the dishes?

PERLMUTTER *shrugs.*

Reconnaissance: negative; no enemy activity. Radio: negative; just dead. No personnel. No blood. No message. Just *(HE waves his arm around)* this. *You tell me.* What happened? *What am I supposed to say in my report?*

PERLMUTTER *(Helpfully)* Polar bears, maybe?

JAKE *(Laughing too loudly, then grabbing his carbine suddenly)* No, the fuckin penguins!

HE *laughs again. Then an awkward silence.* THE MEN *do not understand his nervousness.*

All right, you guys, take it easy. Pull yourselves together. I don't know what gives here, but we got to take it slow, see? *(As if to himself)* Take it slow. *(Looking at* THE MEN *as if they were strangers; almost begging)* You read me? We've got to take it slow. *(*HE *suddenly clutches his chest and falls back into a chair.* HE *has a pained, surprised look on his face as* HE *seems unable to catch his breath)*

HARRY Hey! What's the matter, Sarge? *(Rushing over)* Hey! Sarge! . . . Perlmutter! *Do something?*

PERLMUTTER *gets water out of a canteen.* JAKE *knocks it out of his hand.*

JAKE The air! It's the air! There's no air!

HARRY *(Frantically)* Sarge? What do you mean. There's air all around us. We're *air-regulated.*

JAKE The hatch! *The hatch!*

PERLMUTTER *rushes up the ladder and opens the hatch. A whoosh of air.* JAKE *gradually recovers.*

HARRY Jesus, Jake.

JAKE All right, Perlmutter, shut the fuckin hatch.

PERLMUTTER *comes down slowly.* HARRY *backs up to him.* THEY *look at each other.*

HARRY *(Softly)* Jesus! That's all we need, a stiff!

JAKE Knock it off. I'm okay. I tell you it was the air. There was just something . . . funny . . . about the air. *(*HE *looks around a little distracted, then giggles quietly. As if* HE *is making perfect sense)* Did you guys know I had an aunt Adeline? . . . *Yeah. An aunt*

Adeline. She used to bake apple pies. I'm not *kidding. Real apple pies. Yeah. (*HE *giggles again)*

HARRY *(Looking at* PERLMUTTER) Huh?

PERLMUTTER *shrugs.*

JAKE *(Suddenly looking at them)* Hey, what the hell is this, a goddam conspiracy? I said knock it off.

HARRY *and* PERLMUTTER *busy themselves with their gear.*

HARRY Polar bears. Where do you get that stuff, Perlmutter?

PERLMUTTER *looks at him, then looks away.*

Huh? Where'd you get that stuff?

PERLMUTTER So why not polar bears? Polar bears are quite common in the Arctic regions, Corporal. Polar bears do not live on lettuce. They are carnivores. They have canines. They stalk and kill their prey, Corporal, after which they rip its flesh and consume it. Do you understand? Rip its flesh and consume it. I don't know whether they leave the bones. A polar bear could bite your head off, Corporal, like a lollypop. *(*HE *mimes the act)* And that's only a polar bear. *(*HE *laughs)*

HARRY *(Somewhat frightened)* Yeah? Yeah? You a polar bear expert now? Well, I wouldn't let a polar bear within a hundred feet of me, see.

PERLMUTTER *(After a pause, during which* HE *looks disdainfully at* HARRY*)* Corporal, what makes you think a polar bear would want to get within a hundred feet of you. Within ten feet? What have you got to offer a polar bear? I mean, what have you *really* got to offer a polar bear? A Christian penis? He's a *king,* a king of the snowy waste.

HARRY *(Confused)* What? . . . Yeah? You making a crack? Huh? Huh?

JAKE *(Quietly, as if nothing has been going on)* Now the way I figure it, I figure maybe they went out, got lost, and froze. You know what a dumb bunny that Halberstrand was.

HARRY Yeah. He didn't know his ass from you-know-what.

JAKE And you know the orders. *You* read them. In black and white. *Only* when necessary, and then just topside. Five feet in a storm and you're lost. You don't know where you are. *(A little angrily)* Even without a storm you got to be pretty damn careful. You understand? *Careful.* You can go blind in a second. *(With emphasis)* We got to stick close to the installation. This ain't no Coney Island here.

HARRY Brother Jake, you are speaking the whole truth. *Amen.*

PERLMUTTER But why'd they go out? What for? Where's the bodies? Why'd they leave their rifles, their clothes?

Silence. Sound of clogging toilet.

HARRY You know, this place stinks.

PERLMUTTER *(Examining one of the dishes on the lower bunk, then holding it up)* Sergeant, there's something awful here.

JAKE *grabs the dish away from him, brings it close to his nose, makes a face, and puts it down roughly on the table.*

HARRY What is it?

JAKE It's shit.

HARRY *(After a pause)* Real shit?

JAKE *(Exasperated)* Real shit!

HARRY They were eating shit?

JAKE *(Sitting down somewhat dazed)* Smell it yourself.

HARRY *(Smelling it and giggling nervously)* Jesus. Real shit.

JAKE *(Jumping up angrily)* Well, what the hell did you expect it to be, toy shit?

HARRY Well, hell's bells, Sarge. Gee whiz. Take it easy. It's only shit.

PERLMUTTER *(Poking around in the other dishes)* Hey. Here's some more. It's all over the damn place.

All three MEN *look into every receptacle in a kind of frenzy.* THEY *gradually slow down, sit, and stare at each other.*

HARRY *(Whispering)* Sarge. Sarge. The whole damn place is full of shit. Everything. *(In wonderment)* It's a regular shithouse. They didn't miss a trick.

JACK *(Wearily)* Yeah. They didn't miss a trick.

Sound of clogging toilet. The lights dim.

SCENE 2

The last stages of tidying up. The dishes, pots, and pans have been put away. The trapdoor under the table is open. HARRY, *after several trips with supplies and tools, disappears below.* PERLMUTTER *is checking out the radio and other equipment. Frequency signals, lights, switches.* JAKE, *wearing glasses and wetting his thumb occasionally, is reading through the log. There is a feeling that things are moving along.*

HARRY *(Standing in the pit, his head and shoulders above the floor level)* Phew! That stink just ain't gonna go away. Ma-*ma! (*HE *disappears again. From below)* Damn, it's sure dark down here.

JAKE *(Without looking up)* Get lost.

PERLMUTTER *(Singing)* Shine on / Shine on, harvest moon / Up in the sky / I ain't . . .

JAKE *tosses the log on the table, takes off his glasses, and lights up a cigarette.* PERLMUTTER *stops singing and turns to look at him.*

HARRY *(Popping up)* What's up?

JAKE *(Shrugging)* Perfect. Everything is perfect. Nothing out of order, nothing missing. The usual routine. No mistake, no indication of trouble. Nothing. . . . Nothing. . . . *(Slamming his hand on the table)* Only three goddam men gone without a trace! *(*HE *laughs suddenly)*

HARRY Aw, forget it. We got our own job. You know what jokers those guys were, Sarge. Anything for a laugh. They're probably shacking up with some cold-assed Eskimo.

PERLMUTTER *(Turning)* Maybe . . . maybe they ate each other up.

HE *laughs a little stupidly.* THEY *are silent a minute, as if considering that possibility.*

HARRY *(Laughing)* Ha ha ha! Very good, Perlmutter. You made a funny.

JAKE Shut up.

HARRY He made a *funny.*

JAKE All right, you guys, here's the ticket. *(HE claps his hands once)* We're stuck here for six months. So we better make the best of it. In three weeks we won't be able to go topside anymore. Until then, anyone who goes out takes a carbine and stays within sight. Get me? After that, we stick. . . . Now listen, I don't know any more than you guys. I only know that something's fishy. Maybe we'll find out, maybe we won't. Something made them guys go out when they weren't supposed to. But that ain't gonna happen to us. If we stick, we're okay. We take every precaution. That understood?

HARRY Sure, Sarge. We stick.

THEY *are all silent a minute.*

PERLMUTTER But how do we know they went out?

JAKE *(Through his teeth)* Oh, knock it off, Perlmutter. I don't want any of your crap here, understand? *(Suddenly, with unwarranted irritation) Don't you bug me, Perlmutter!*

PERLMUTTER Okay. Okay, okay. Take it easy. I was only asking.

JAKE Don't ask.

PERLMUTTER Okay, okay. I won't ask.

HARRY *(Laughing suddenly)* They ate each other up! Oh, you dumb bunny. *(HE laughs again, stops abruptly, not quite satisfied with himself)* You know, I don't like living with a goddamned mystery.

JAKE *(After a pause, ignoring HARRY's remark)* All right. So that's it. We stick. Keep your noses clean. It'll work out. We've got a great organization behind us. We stick to the routine day and night. We follow orders. We go by the book. *By the book!* We keep cool. Harry, you handle the supplies. Perlmutter, you take the technical angle. And me—*(HE smiles)* I'll do the worrying.

HARRY Oh, yeah, yeah, yeah.

JAKE We split the cooking. I'll have a duty roster tomorrow.

Sound of clogging toilet.

And corporal! Fix that goddamned toilet!

HARRY *(Jumping out of the pit)* Righto!

HE *enters the toilet, from which hammering can be heard throughout the following scene.*

JAKE Okay, Perlmutter. Let's make contact. You set?

PERLMUTTER Right.

HE *turns several dials, flicks switches. A few lights go on, others blink. Some radio static.*

Station 2-5-Y-00 calling Hornpipe. Station 2-5-Y-00 calling Hornpipe. Do you read us?

A few moments of static.

Station 2-5-Y-00 calling Hornpipe. Station 2-5-Y-00 calling Hornpipe. Do you read us?

RADIO Hello. Hello. This is Hornpipe. This is Hornpipe. We are reading you loud and clear. We are reading you loud and clear. You are overdue. Repeat: you are overdue. Over.

PERLMUTTER Okay, Sarge.

JAKE *gives him a sheet of paper.*

Hello, Hornpipe. Hello, Hornpipe. Preliminary report. Arrived destination safe supplies 0700. Installation intact. No sign personnel. No indication ultimate disposition. All equipment working order. Reports will follow daily. Precautions taken. Over. Over.

Static. To JAKE:

What precautions?

JAKE *touches his head. Static.*

RADIO Hello, Station 2-5-Y-00. Report received. Repeat: report received. Stand by. Stand by. Over.

PERLMUTTER *(Raising his eyebrow)* What do you think's up?

JAKE How the hell should I know. . . . Maybe weather info.

RADIO *(Static)* Hello, Station 2-5-Y-00. Request further information disposition personnel. Request further information disposition personnel. Over.

PERLMUTTER *looks at* JAKE, *who is hesitating.*

JAKE All right, damn it, tell them. *(*HE *gives him another sheet of paper)*

PERLMUTTER Station 2-5-Y-00 calling Hornpipe. Station 2-5-Y-00 calling Hornpipe. Are you there?

RADIO Come in Station 2-5-Y-00. Come in. This is Hornpipe.

PERLMUTTER Further details disposition personnel. Further details disposition personnel. All, repeat, all utensils utilized personnel preservation feces.

JAKE Christ.

HARRY *(finally)* Jake, do you think it's any different for them?

JAKE Who?

HARRY Kikes?

JAKE Do I think *what's* different?

HARRY Jerking off.

JAKE *gives him a long hard look.*

Well, I mean, you know . . .

JAKE *And why are you asking me, huh? Why are you asking me?*

HARRY *quickly puts out his light and rolls toward the wall.*

HARRY Jake, I'm sleeping. Good night.

JAKE *tries to read but cannot and puts the book down with exasperation.* HE *puts out his light and tosses and turns for several minutes, shaking all three bunks. Silence.*

HARRY *(Softly)* Jake?

JAKE What?

HARRY Is it true that Chink girls go sideways? *(No answer)* Jake? *(No answer)* Jake, I'm going to sleep.

THEY *fall asleep. Sound of clogged toilet. Silence. Suddenly,* JAKE *leaps out of his bed and switches on the lights.*

JAKE All right, all right, turn out! I've had it. Get up! *(*HE *shakes the* OTHERS*)* Get up, you guys.

PERLMUTTER What the hell's the matter with you, man? You crazy? Quit picking on me!

JAKE *drags* PERLMUTTER *out of his bunk, then* HARRY, *after which* HE *pulls out all the bedding furiously, throwing his on the bottom bunk and the others' each up a bunk.* PERLMUTTER *and* HARRY *look at each other briefly in bewilderment.*

HARRY It's happened. He's cracked.

JAKE Six weeks I've had it and I'm not taking it any more. Not one goddamn more night. From now on I sleep here. *(*HE *pats the bottom bunk)*

HARRY Hey, what's eating you? You *took* the top bunk. Nobody twisted your arm. You *took* it. What the hell's eating you?

JAKE Farts! That's what's eating me. Big fat smelly farts! I'm choking to death. I can't breathe. Every night I go to sleep, nice and easy, and every goddamn night you two guys start farting away. Boom! Boom! Or just the long soft slow ones, the ones that got the real stink. I'm sleeping in a goddamn cloud of fart. It's getting so I can't sleep waiting for it. One minute it's okay, and the next minute it's creeping up the wall, over the blankets, *coming in for the kill.* I can't stand it any more! I feel trapped! *(*HE *pauses)* What the hell are you guys doing? How do you manage to fart so much? I mean, any guy will fart a little, even dames. But you guys fart *all the time. (*HE *sits down in exasperation, then giggles nervously)* No, no more. No more. All right. From now on you guys smell my farts. I'll try to be considerate. I'll squeeze them out slowly. Christ! *(*HE *giggles again)*

HARRY Damn white of you.

JAKE Make your goddamn bunk.

HARRY *grudgingly makes his bunk.* PERLMUTTER *stands there, fuming.*

What's eating you?

PERLMUTTER *(Explosively)* You are an anti-Semite! You are an anti-Semite! An anti-*Semite!* An anti-*Semite!* You—

JAKE *gets up and slaps him once.* PERLMUTTER *stops, looks at him briefly, then goes to the top bunk, hastily makes his bed, climbs in and goes to sleep.* JAKE *and* HARRY *shrug at each other and follow suit.* THEY *gradually settle, become quiet, and finally only the sound of breathing is heard. Then a loud crack, like ice breaking. The room shakes, and its joints groan.* PERLMUTTER *wakes up screaming.*

PERLMUTTER It's coming! It's coming!

JAKE Christ! What now?

HARRY Oh, what the hell now?

PERLMUTTER It's coming! It's coming! *(*HE *laughs hysterically)* It's coming!

JAKE *and* HARRY *put on their lights.* HARRY *stands up and shakes* PERLMUTTER. JAKE *leans out from his bunk.*

JAKE Easy, boy. Easy.

HARRY Hey, Perl, cut it out, will you? You scared me. You're giving me the creeps lately. You really are.

PERLMUTTER *(Nervously to* HARRY, *as* HE *clutches him)* My father . . . *(*HE *gulps)* is Abraham. My father . . . is Abraham! My father . . . is *Abraham!* Did you know that? . . . I didn't. I didn't know that. My father . . . is Abraham. *(*HE *pauses. As a revelation)* And I am Isaac! Isaac! Isaac!

HARRY Sure, sure. My dad's Ed. Eddie. Edward.

PERLMUTTER No! He's Abraham! *(Whispering suddenly)* Don't you feel it? *(*JAKE *and* HARRY *look at each other)* Don't you feel it? Listen. *(Agitated)* It, it . . . grabbed me. *(*HE *clutches* HARRY *more closely)* No, it touched me. It . . . it wanted to . . . suck me in. *(A short giggle)* It was waiting. It's waiting.

HARRY *(Pleading, in an urgent whisper)* Aw, cut it out, Perl. Cut it *out. (In a normal voice)* You're scaring the shit outa me!

PERLMUTTER *(Raising himself, sternly)* I tell you it's coming! We must prepare! Prepare! *(Suddenly smiling)* Oh, how I ache! How I ache! Do you know how I ache?

JAKE Shit!

PERLMUTTER *(Laughs, then stops abruptly)* Gentile fools! I tell you it's all around us. We're inside it. It's eating us up! . . . *(Laughing)* But I love it! I know I love it! *Looove!* Do you hear me? . . . Oh, you poor puny fools. Children! Don't you know? We are children! . . . The time is coming. Coming! And I am ready! Readyyyy!

JAKE *(Poking* PERLMUTTER *gently)* Come off it, man. You been seeing too many movies. You been dreaming.

PERLMUTTER *(Whispering)* Yes! Yes, that's it! Dreaming. And now I'm awake. Awake! *(Shouting joyously)* My father! My fatherrr! Do you hear meeee!

HARRY Is he nuts, Sarge?

JAKE *(Without conviction)* Bats.

PERLMUTTER *(Clutching* HARRY*)* It's something you don't know about.

HARRY *(Faintly)* What?

PERLMUTTER *shakes his head.* JAKE *leaps off his bunk, grabs a carbine and hands it to* PERLMUTTER.

JAKE Here. Sleep with it. It's loaded.

PERLMUTTER *(*HE *shakes his head. Then rhetorically, as if to a jury)* Gentlemen, won't you have pity on this poor boy? He is a good boy, a kind boy, a gentle boy. Whatever his crime, however hideous, remember the extenuations, which are many. Do not, I beg you, do not piss on him. *(*HE *laughs, rolls over, and falls asleep)*

HARRY *and* JAKE *look at each other.*

HARRY *(Without conviction)* Ha ha. He made a funny.

JAKE Perlmutter. Are you okay, Perlmutter? Huh? You okay? *(No answer. To* HARRY*)* Nightmare. Let's hit the sack.

HARRY *hesitates.*

That's an order!

THEY *go to bed, turn off their lights, and toss a minute. Then silence.*

HARRY *(Softly)* Jake? *(No answer)* What did he mean? *(No answer. Silence, then breathing)* Jake? Who's Adeline? Who's Aunt Adeline?

Sound of wind above. Sound of clogged toilet.

SCENE 4

The three MEN *have just finished a meal.* THEY *are lounging and smoking.* JAKE *is playing solitaire.* PERLMUTTER *is lost in his thoughts, rocking slightly back and forth like one of the orthodox.*

HARRY *(Dancing around with an imaginary woman)* Well, boys, three more lousy months to go. *(*HE *kisses her several times)* Yes, sir, three more lousy months. *(Neither of the other two responds)* When I get back, know what I'm gonna do? *(*HE *waits)* Don't, huh? Well, you can shove it, for all I care. . . . I'm gonna trade in my old heap, that's what. Get a new car. Get me a new car, boys. *(*HE *waits. No response)* A new Merc. And boy, will I be sitting pretty. Dames galore. . . . You don't think so? Huh? You don't think they'll go for me? Listen, they'll go. I ain't so bad. Did you know I made it with Corinne week before we left? You didn't know, did you? Well, I did. Man, was she surprised. Wanted more, too. . . . Ah, the hell with you, Jake. This place is making you . . . Why the hell don't you talk? *(Silence. Then, furiously, an abrupt shift of mood) Why don't you talk!!! (No response. Nervous,* HE *walks back and forth)* Well, I just mean why don't you talk?

JAKE *and* PERLMUTTER *suddenly giggle.*

You're both batty. Couple of nuts. *(Silence)*

PERLMUTTER *(Fervently, looking up)* Oh, my God.

JAKE *stops playing solitaire, but doesn't look at him.*

Oh, my God! *(Slowly, as if with effort)* I am thy *creature.* I am thy *creature!*

HE *sobs softly.* JAKE *gathers up his cards, holding the deck concavely in his palm, and slowly lets them spring out on the floor. There is static on radio, and a* VOICE, *different from the one they've heard—metallic, mocking, always on the verge of laughter.*

RADIO Roger Wilco. Roger Wilco. Roger Wilco. Roger Wilco.

JAKE God damn it, Perlmutter, I told you never to leave the set on when we aren't in contact.

HARRY Hell, leave it on. Maybe we'll get some Eskimo music. I'm just about ready for it.

RADIO Roger Wilco. Roger Wilco. And now, a musical interlude.

A long pause, then a clash of cymbals followed by cataclysmic thunder and lightning. The latter actually flashes through the installation. Then weird electronic sounds, broken by blasts of thunder and lightning, all of which seems to take place in the installation. JAKE *jumps up and throws several switches off on the radio, then sits down in relief.*

HARRY Wow. Christ Almighty.

RADIO *(Belching forth a cosmic laughter which shakes the whole installation)* Roger Wilco! Roger Wilco! Roger Wilco! *(Laughter again)*

PERLMUTTER *(Dropping to his knees)* Oh, Lord, I am thy *creature!* Forgive me! I am thy *creature!*

Silence. JAKE *and* HARRY *are shaken.*

HARRY You're a creature all right. He's nuts, Jake. He did it. He's playing a trick on us, he's going to kill us, he's just waiting for the chance, he's watching all the time—

JAKE Shut up! . . . Let me think.

HARRY Think? About *what?*

RADIO *(Interrupting, this time with the old voice)* Hornpipe calling Station 2-5-Y-00 Hornpipe calling Station 2-5-Y-00. Urgent. Repeat: urgent. Come in if you are there.

JAKE *and* HARRY *are too stunned to move.*

Come in, please. Use disaster frequency if necessary. Imperative establish contact again. Repeat: imperative . . . *(Static)* . . . otherwise presumption dead. Over. Over. Over.

HARRY Dead? *(*HE *giggles nervously)* Jake? Hear that? Presumption dead? *(*HE *giggles again)* We're not dead.

JAKE *(Hesitates a moment. Then, grabbing* PERLMUTTER *and dragging him to the radio)* Answer! Answer, you bastard, or I'll kill you! What did you do? Tell me!

HE *grabs a knife and holds the sharp edge to* PERLMUTTER*'s throat.* PERLMUTTER *smiles.*

Answer!

PERLMUTTER *sits by the radio and turns the knobs and switches.*

PERLMUTTER Station 2-5-Y-00 calling Hornpipe. Station 2-5-Y-00 calling Hornpipe. Request clarification. Contact has been daily. Repeat: contact has been daily. Disaster frequency unnecessary. Over.

RADIO *(Flute trills, then the* SECOND VOICE. *A loud burp)* Roger Wilco. Roger Wilco. Roger Poger. Wilko Bilko. *(Laughter)*

JAKE *(Swinging his hand on the set)* Damn! Damn! Damn you!

PERLMUTTER *turns halfway around and gives him a faint smile.*

RADIO *(Mocking)* Repeat: Roger Wilco. Roger Wilco.

Again the hideous cosmic laughter, which shakes the whole installation, then silence. JAKE *throws the table aside, lifts the trapdoor, and points to* HARRY.

JAKE Everything. Check everything. Fast! It's got to be something here.

HARRY *(Happily)* Right, Sarge. That's the way. We'll lick it. *(*HE *jumps into the pit, disappears, screams)* Jake! *(*HE *sticks his head up, but whereas before his shoulders and chest were above the floor, now only his head shows)* Jake, look. *(Holding his hands up, whimpering)* Lift me up, Jake. Please!

JAKE *(Taking the knife)* Check it.

HARRY Jake. Jake. *(*HE *slowly lowers his head)*

JAKE *sits in a chair. After a minute,* PERLMUTTER *turns to face him.*

PERLMUTTER *(With a queer smile)* Well, Sergeant, only eight more weeks and we'll be leaving this . . . fuckin place. *(*HE *giggles)*

JAKE *(After a pause)* And wouldn't you hate that?

THEY *stare at each other a minute.*

You don't want to go back, do you?

PERLMUTTER . . . Do you, Sergeant?

JAKE Why shouldn't I?

PERLMUTTER That's for you to say, isn't it?

THEY *stare at each other again.*

JAKE You know I'm going to report you, don't you?

PERLMUTTER *(After a long pause)* To whom? That is the question, isn't it? *(*JAKE *does not answer)* You think I'm crazy?

JAKE Aren't you?

PERLMUTTER Yes. Mad. Insane. Psycho. *(Whispering)* So are you, Sergeant.

JAKE The hell I am!

PERLMUTTER It's too bad, Sergeant, that you're not a Jew.

JAKE Why?

PERLMUTTER You're too cocky.

JAKE You Jews ain't cocky?

PERLMUTTER You're a man, Sergeant. Just a man.

JAKE Why don't you shut up? *(*HE *begins picking up the cards)*

PERLMUTTER *(After a long pause)* It isn't enough, is it?

JAKE What?

PERLMUTTER Being a man.

JAKE You're crazy, Perlmutter.

THEY *are silent a minute.* JAKE *is obviously waiting for* PERLMUTTER *to say more.*

PERLMUTTER The other night . . . I heard you.

JAKE *(Pretending surprise)* What? . . . *(Hissing)* Shut up!

PERLMUTTER You were whimpering.

JAKE Shut up, you . . .

PERLMUTTER I wanted to . . . talk to you . . . but you're . . . so cocky.

JAKE *(Half-rising, in a violent whisper)* I'm not going to tell you again. Just shut up! You bug me! Why? Why?

PERLMUTTER I'm not afraid of you . . . Sergeant. I could have sworn you cried. Did you? Don't be ashamed. I'm not . . . And what was that mumbling? Pr—

JAKE Shut up! I told you—

PERLMUTTER *(Sharply)* Sit down. Go on, sit down.

JAKE *sits down.*

It didn't do any good, did it? You don't believe them any more. But you wanted to say *something.* There was something you couldn't express. You felt . . . helpless.

JAKE *(In a monotone)* I don't know what you're talking about.

PERLMUTTER No. Who would? It's a private agony. . . . We are a brotherhood of mute sufferers, dressed always for Mardi Gras, smiling, dancing, boasting. But inside, we bleed . . . Jake. We play the fool. All of us. Shall I show you?

JAKE Keep your damn Jew thoughts to yourself.

PERLMUTTER All right.

JAKE, *disconcerted, moves as if to speak, but is prevented by* HARRY, *who sticks his head up.*

HARRY Hey, Sarge, look at this.

HE *holds up a few scraps of paper.* JAKE *reaches out.*

Careful. They're a little shitty. Must have used it for toilet paper. But there's writing on them.

JAKE *hesitates, then takes them gingerly and lays them on the table. They are silent.*

PERLMUTTER Go on, Jake. Read them.

HARRY *looks at* PERLMUTTER, *then* JAKE, *in bewilderment.*

JAKE *(Reading)* Feb. 2. Down to two men. Henley has disappeared. Radio all out. *He's driving us mad!* Help us. Feb. 9. Have not been to toilet in over week. Stench unbearable. No dishes left. Bancroft emptied his carbine into latrine last night.

HARRY *(Interrupting)* Huh?

JAKE *(Repeating)* . . . into latrine last night. No good. He never lets us alone. We are being crushed. Feb. 14. Bancroft did . . . unspeakable things. I . . . can't believe it. I . . . was unprepared. He was . . . a great man. I wanted . . . What will . . . my mother . . .

HARRY That don't make sense. *(Looks around at the walls)*

JAKE It's smudged. The paper is smudged.

THEY *are silent again.*

HARRY Read the rest.

JAKE Feb. 20. I am alone now. Just he and I. I hear him all the time. I can't stand the . . . laughing. My head is exploding. What a fool I . . . we . . . Feb. 26. Oh, God . . . March 2. Tell Ginger . . .

HARRY *(Finally)* That's all?

No answer. Sound of clogged toilet. HARRY *turns his head slowly and looks at the toilet door.*

SCENE 5

Morning. An alarm goes off. No one stirs for a long time. Finally HARRY *and* JAKE *rouse themselves and dress, while* PERLMUTTER *stares from his bunk. No one uses the toilet.*

HARRY I'm gonna *(*HE *yawns)* go bugs if I don't see the outside soon.

PERLMUTTER *laughs wildly.*

Yeah, that's right. Bugs like him. How are we going to explain *him* when we get relieved? Huh? Shell shock? He'll never last the four weeks. Tell 'em he got homesick? Boy, that's a laugh. Homesick.

PERLMUTTER *(Laughs again)* You're mad, man.

HARRY Jake, why don't you stop him? I tell you he gives me the creeps. You hear him at night. Bela Lugosi crossed with Boris Karloff.

JAKE Why the hell don't you shut up. Go on in and piss.

HARRY No, you go. I'll be a gent.

JAKE *(A little angrily)* Go on in and piss.

HARRY *(Petulantly)* I don't wanna. *(After a pause)* I don't have to anyway.

JAKE *looks at him.*

I mean . . . I just don't have to yet.

JAKE What are you, saving it up for your birthday candles?

HARRY Look, Sarge, no hard feelings, but if you have to piss, you go right ahead and piss. You worry about your piss and I'll worry about mine. Okay?

JAKE *continues to dress.*

Well, ain't you going?

JAKE You worrying about my piss now?

HARRY You do what the hell you like.

JAKE *(Sarcastically)* Hey, big man.

HARRY *sulks.*

Who's got breakfast duty this morning?

HARRY You do.

JAKE I had it yesterday.

HARRY Perl had it.

JAKE The hell he did. *(HE goes to the duty roster, then begins fussing noisily at the stove. After a minute HE begins looking for something, at first casually, then frantically)* Where the hell's the frying pan? Perlmutter, where's the frying pan?

At first there is no response from PERLMUTTER, *then* HE *points.* JAKE *yanks the pan out from under the stove, not realizing there is something in it. When* HE *does* HE *stops short, is silent for a few seconds, then puts it on the table and stares at it.* HE *giggles softly.*

S.O.S. Look. The real thing.

HE *continues giggling.* HARRY *stands without expression.* PERLMUTTER *is smiling in sympathy. Suddenly* JAKE *turns to him and knocks him out of his bunk with a blow to the head, then sits on him and, still giggling, begins pounding him.*

Oh, you funny bastard! Oh, you funny bastard. S.O.S. *Shit! . . . Oh, mother! . . .*

HARRY *(Restraining* JAKE *with difficulty)* Jake, stop it! Stop! You'll kill him! Please! Jake!

JAKE *goes on pounding* PERLMUTTER.

Jake, listen. *(Shouting)* He didn't do it! I did!

JAKE *(Continues to pound* PERLMUTTER *a few seconds, then stops)* Wha-what? . . . You did it? *You?* YOU?

HARRY Jake, I couldn't help it. Honest. I was scared! He made me scared.

JAKE *slowly gets to his feet.*

Jake! Jake!

JAKE *hurls him against the latrine door.*

JAKE Get in there and *piss!* Get in there and *piss! (*HE *moves menacingly toward* HARRY*)*

HARRY *(Half-crawling into the latrine)* No, Jake. No . . . no . . . You . . . I . . .

HE *shakes his head as the door closes on him.* JAKE *stands dumbly in the middle of the room.*

PERLMUTTER *(Weakly)* Sergeant?

JAKE *snaps out of his mood, quickly gets the first-aid equipment and revives* PERLMUTTER.

JAKE Sorry, Perlmutter. Lost my head. I . . . made a mistake.

PERLMUTTER One more mistake won't hurt, Sergeant.

JAKE Oh, shut up, will you?

PERLMUTTER You hit me very hard.

JAKE Yeah.

PERLMUTTER But I feel better now. *(*HE *puts his hand on* JAKE*'s arm)* I'll try and establish contact, Sergeant.

THEY *look at each other.*

Please.

JAKE No. No more of that crap, I told you. No more.

PERLMUTTER *(Anxiously)* Sergeant, I'll try to establish radio contact. It's important. . . . Trust me.

THEY *stare at each other in silence a moment.*

JAKE Oh, what the hell do I care? Do what you like.

PERLMUTTER It's important, Jake. You won't regret it.

JAKE Yeah . . . yeah.

JAKE *gets up, lies on his bunk, and lights a cigarette.* PERLMUTTER *slowly rises from the floor, straightens himself out thoroughly, then combs his hair.* HE *sits down by the radio timidly, seems excited, turns the switches and speaks.*

PERLMUTTER Hello, hello, this is Station o-o-o-oo calling Hornpipe. Repeat: this is Station o-o-o-oo calling Hornpipe. Are you . . . there?

RADIO *(The original* VOICE, *desperately)* Hello! Hello! Are you Station—*(Flute trills, then the* SECOND VOICE*)* Roger Wilco. Roger Wilco. Come in Station o-o-o-oo. This is Hornpipe. I am your baby.*(*HE *relaxes, turns briefly to* JAKE *with an exultant smile, then begins his message)*

PERLMUTTER I read you, Station Hornpipe, I read you. Have you any message?

Static. The toilet flushes. The door opens slowly. JAKE *sits up tensely.* HARRY *comes out, sinks into a chair limply and does not move.*

JAKE *(Softly)* Atta boy, Harry. We'll make it.

RADIO *(Loudly, then normal volume)* Roger Wilco! Roger Wilco! . . . Yes, I have a message. My message is—have *you* any message? *(Raucous laughter, which shakes the installation completely)*

PERLMUTTER Hello! Hello! Station o-o-o-oo calling Hornpipe. Urgent. Repeat: urgent.

RADIO *(Unctuously)* Come in Station o-o-o-oo.

PERLMUTTER We are in desperate straits. Repeat: we are in desperate straits. The moment . . . is precarious.

JAKE Wha-?

PERLMUTTER The moment is precarious. Future: dim. Repeat: future: dim. Can you help us? Over. *(Electronic sounds, static, then the* VOICE, *as if coming from a great distance, gaining volume as it gets closer)*

RADIO rogerwilcorogerwilcorogerwilcorogerwilcorogerwilcorogerwilcoROGERWILCOROGERWILCOROGERWILCOROGERWILCO—ROGER WILCO! *(Normal volume)* Your message has been received. Your message has been received. Follow instructions without fail. . . . You must cast more pearl to the swine. Repeat: cast more pearl to the swine. *(A long pause)* Pluck out your eyes. Pluck out your eyes. *(Another pause)* Eat offal, eat offal *(The voice fades)* eat offal, eat offal . . . *(Faintly)* Do you read me? Over.

PERLMUTTER *(After a long pause)* Over. *(*HE *appears for a moment to be having difficulty swallowing, to be almost choking. Then)* Message . . . received. Over. Over. *(Gagging)* Ooover. Olulover. Olulover. Lululaluover. *(Mixed with giggling)* Ululanilanunover. Lulululukurakolalova. *(*HE *continues in the same manner, like one who has the gift of tongues—glossolalia—alternating gibberish and giggling, a joyous kind of giggling)*

JAKE *(Jumping down from his bunk and shaking him)* Perlmutter! For God's sake, stop it!

PERLMUTTER *(Stopping abruptly)* I'm quite all right, Sergeant. I have good news. I got through. We are to be saved. Do you hear, Sergeant? Saved! I got through. *(*HE *gets up and walks away from* JAKE*)* Oh, Harry. Glad to have you on board again. You see, there's no danger. I'll show you. *(*HE *opens the toilet door, enters, comes out again part way)* It's a fuckin human world, don't you think? What? . . . Cheerio. *(*HE *shuts the door behind him)*

JAKE *and* HARRY *are still for a long time. Finally* JAKE *takes a seat near* HARRY. HARRY *looks at him.*

HARRY What's gonna happen, Jake? What's it all about?

JAKE *shakes his head.*

Jake, you're in charge. What's the S.O.P.?

JAKE *shakes his head again.* THEY *lapse into another silence.*

You know, when I was in there . . . it was strange. I . . . that's the only way I can put it. Strange. I don't know why. I just felt it was. It was like . . . well, you know . . . I didn't feel *human.* I mean . . . oh, what the hell. I don't know. I didn't feel like . . . very . . . You know what I mean? Huh? Just sitting there on the throne. I mean I was scared and all that but . . . I mean them notes and all, but . . . well, it was . . . different. Oh, hell. Jake?

JAKE *does not respond. Sound of clogged toilet.*

I wish I could explain to you, Jake . . . Do you . . .

THEY *lapse into another silence. Sound of clogged toilet. A sharp crack.*

It was funny, Jake. Do you think it's anything? I really, really . . . really . . . (HE *shakes his head)* Funny. Something awful funny . . . Hey, Jake, will you say something?

JAKE *(Almost inaudibly)* I gotta piss.

HARRY What? You gotta kiss?

JAKE *(Shouting)* I gotta piss! (HE *stands up and faces the door)* Oh, God, how I gotta piss! . . . Perlmutter! I gotta piss, damn you! Come out! Come out! *(There is no reply)* Perlmuttaaa! Perlmuttaaa! *(Suddenly* HE *rushes forward and kicks open the door.* HE *stops abruptly when he sees that the toilet, what he can see of it, is empty)* Perlmutter, you coming out or do I come in and get you? Do you hear me? I gotta piss *now!* I'm *ready!*

HARRY Jake.

JAKE *Perlmutta!* I'm warning you. *(No response.* JAKE *backs away to the wall.* HE *takes a carbine out of his bunk, shoves a bullet into the chamber, and stands ready. At the top of his lungs) Perlmutter! I'm coming! I'm coming!*

HE *stalks the toilet, firing bullets into it as he advances. The lights dim as he passes through the door and disappears, still firing.*

HARRY Jake!

SCENE 6

Dishes, pots, pans scattered about, as in the first scene. Sound of clogged toilet. HARRY *alone, writing. After a while,* HE *reads, then talks as* HE *writes.*

HARRY . . . *home* . . . I miss Jake. It is nine days now. I pushed food in five days ago. It is still there . . . I feel so lonely . . . and yet . . . not . . . unhappy. I think of Perlmutter a lot and try to remember all those crazy things he said. But I can't. He was a strange guy. *(*HE *puts his head on his arm)* Jake. Jake. Oh, God, Jake. What do I do now? *How* do I do it?

A sharp, wrenching crack, as if the earth itself were splitting. Insistent clogging of the toilet. HE *rises. Once or twice he seems on the verge of going into the toilet.* HE *holds his head.*

God, it stinks!

HE *removes the trap door in the floor, is overwhelmed by the smell, and puts it back.* HE *returns to the table, sits, and finally writes again.*

Mmmmmmmm. Mmmmmmmmmm. If anything happens, tell Perlmutter's dad Abraham that he was . . . okay. He was a good soldier. I guess Jake would want Flo to know that . . .

HE *looks up, then abruptly rips up the sheet he has been writing on and scatters the pieces on the floor. Static. No voice.* HE *writes again.*

He has been trying all the time to get me. But I don't know enough about the radio. He tells me . . . terrible things. He, he . . . breathes on me all the time. I know it sounds crazy, but it's true. *(Looking up)* You're not here. You don't know. He does. *(Writing again)* And, and yet, even though he wants to, to . . . get me, I get the feeling he . . . (HE *giggles. Then, to himself)* Wow. Wait'll they get a load of this. They'll never believe it.

HE *giggles again. Another sharp crack. The installation rumbles. Insistent sound of clogged toilet.* HE *stands.*

Damn you!

Again the sharp crack and sound of clogged toilet. Half crying:

Damn you! Damn you! They'll get you, whoever you are. They'll get you!

A sharp crack. HE *is knocked on the floor almost into the latrine. Sound of clogged toilet. Crying softly:*

Oh, Jake, Jake. Help me. I'm so tired . . .

SCENE 7

HARRY *alone, sitting in the middle of the room, leaning on a carbine.* HE *looks exhausted. Greenish light.*

HARRY It's all right, Jake. It's all right. I'm okay. *(His head drops.* HE *raises it slowly)* It's all right. Mommy, it's all right. It's all right . . . Our father, full of grace . . . *(*HE *giggles, then is silent)* It's all right. It's all right. I got it all figured out. *(*HE *giggles)* And I feel good. Oh, I feel good. Damn good. *(*HE *giggles again, then stops. Half rising, almost in a whisper)* I feel wonderful. I feel . . . peaceful. *(Raising his head and shaking it)* Oh, I feel good!

HE *stops as if paralyzed, then swings the carbine around and shoots a bullet in his head. As the lights dim, the same devastating crack and the sound of a clogged toilet.*

SCENE 8

Empty installation. Thuds above, then voices. The hatch is opened. A smoke bomb is dropped. When the smoke clears, THREE MEN *quickly descend and search the place. Then* THEY *relax, take off their clothes.*

LIEUTENANT Take this down, Sergeant.

The SERGEANT *fumbles for a pad.*

Arrived destination *(*HE *looks at his watch)* 0715. No immediate sign personnel.

SERGEANT Yes, sir. *(*HE *waits expectantly)*

LIEUTENANT Er, that's all for now, Sergeant.

SERGEANT Yes, sir.

Sound of clogged toilet.

LIEUTENANT Take note of that, Sergeant.

SERGEANT Yes, sir.

LIEUTENANT *(Walking around, inspecting)* Dirty buggers, weren't they? *(*HE *stops, picks up a dish, smells)* Sergeant . . . what do you make of this?

SERGEANT *(Taking the dish and smelling several times)* Well, sir. Can't say, sir.

LIEUTENANT Corporal Watkins!

CORPORAL WATKINS *(Snapping to attention)* Yes, sir!

LIEUTENANT Get cracking on that radio.

CORPORAL WATKINS Yes, sir. *(*HE *goes to the radio and begins turning dials and pulling switches)*

LIEUTENANT *(Picking up another dish and sniffing)* Sergeant, what do you make of *this?*

SERGEANT *(Smelling dish)* Well . . . I can't be sure, sir, but it does . . .

LIEUTENANT *(Leaping to several other receptacles)* And these? What the hell . . . Sergeant . . .

CORPORAL WATKINS Contact, sir.

LIEUTENANT What? Oh. Good. Proceed. *(*HE *takes out a pipe and begins lighting it)*

CORPORAL WATKINS Station 2-5-Y-00 calling Hornpipe. Station 2-5-Y-00 calling Hornpipe. Come in Hornpipe. Come in.

RADIO Roger Wilco. Roger Wilco. Hello, are you there yet, my pets?

THEY *all look at one another.*

LIEUTENANT *(Slowly)* What the hell was that?

THEY *look at one another again. Sound of clogged toilet. The lights dim.*

KENNETH BERNARD was born in Brooklyn in 1930 and lived until he was fourteen in Framingham, Massachusetts. He graduated from New York's High School of Commerce, received his bachelor's degree from the City College of New York, served two years as a private in the U.S. Army, and went on to Columbia University. There he received his M.A. and Ph.D., writing his doctoral dissertation on the work of the American Gothic novelist Charles Brockden Brown. His scholarly criticism, poetry, and short stories have been published in such periodicals as *Antioch Review, The Massachusetts Review, Mundus Artium, The Paris Review,* and *Prism International;* an entire issue of *The Minnesota Review* was recently devoted to his novel *The Maldive Chronicles.* Mr. Bernard's plays have been produced by such organizations as the New Theatre Workshop, the Actors Studio Playwrights Unit, the Chelsea Theatre Center in Brooklyn, and most notably by John Vaccaro's Play-House of the Ridiculous. Mr. Bernard presently teaches American Literature at Long Island University, and lives in New York with his wife and three children.